Poems

for

Circle Time

and

Literacy Hour

MARGARET GOLDTHORPE

Poems for Circle Time and Literacy Hour
LL01116
ISBN 1 85503 269 4
© Margaret Goldthorpe
© illustrations Gary Taylor
All rights reserved
First published 1998

LDA, Duke Street, Wisbech, Cambs, PE13 2AE

Contents

Foreword by
Jenny Mosley

I feel extraordinarily fortunate. Having, since the early seventies thoroughly enjoyed classroom teaching I then, in 1986, became 'freelance' in order to further pioneer and develop the Quality Circle Time Model in a wide range of schools.

Because schools are responding so enthusiastically to all the recommendations of QCT, I was able to train other teachers to help me support the development of the model across the UK. I now have a small team of highly qualified, well trained, enthusiastic and wonderfully successful consultants. Any of 'their' schools will testify to the exciting quality and range of their specialist skills.

Margaret Goldthorpe is one of these consultants. She is a shining example of many amazing qualities. She has four young, highly energetic and creative children and she actively supports her husband, Dennis, in his constantly expanding and exciting special school. She teaches in a school weekly and dashes around the UK sensitively and humorously, supporting schools to meet the challenges of what she often refers to as the 'Golden Model'!

Her good nature, kindness and insightfulness also shine through the poems. They made me grin, sigh and generally want to rush back into the classroom to gather children round to enjoy them. The Circle Time 'Scripts' have been delicately structured so as to help children really feel relaxed and safe enough to explore a range of moral values. She captures through her use of 'I', the turbulent, sensitive inner world of the child. The poems are charming and they have a rhythm, an accuracy and a simplicity that will attract children and teachers alike. They will warm up many a heart in many a Circle Time.

As well as being stimulating and provocative, *Poems for Circle Time and Literacy Hour,* also has the unique advantage of building meaningful bridges between Circle Time and the curriculum. I am confident that it will be a tremendously helpful resource for those teachers who are dedicated to both literacy and emotional literacy.

Acknowledgements

For the last three years I have travelled the country running INSET for teachers. Some of these days have been just for teachers, on days when the school is closed to children, and some have been days when the school is open and I have gone in to demonstrate Circle Time with children.

So I should first like to thank the children who have participated in these Circle Times. Never believe the newspapers who try to tell you that children's behaviour is going to the dogs. Over these three years I have been unfailingly impressed by the children's excellent behaviour and their thoughtful, perceptive response to the challenges of Circle Time.

I have come to recognise more and more that we should sit and talk with children about their problems and difficulties, as they frequently have better solutions than we do to their problems.

However, having said that, there is another whole book of out-takes that could be written of all the hilarious, off-the-wall Circle Time suggestions that have been made during my travels!

So I should also like to thank all of the teachers who have been kind enough to lend me their children to be demonstrated upon. And who have been unfazed by, as in the case of one school, being told that as a result of the demonstration Circle Time they have to go back to their classroom and make a four-foot swingometer to register classroom noise; or, in the case of another school, they have to allow children to take turns at being the child who will stand up and bash a gong every time classroom noise gets too much!

All this chaos and more have I left behind me!

Thanks, I have had fun!

I should also like to thank the inventors of the Circle Time games – but, alas, that is not always possible. I have been taught them by teachers, by support staff and by children.

However: I should like to thank:

Donna Barratt née Bennett, Lys Kirby, Les Olive, Paul Casey, Joan Mellor and Jo Healey, all of the Harrow Primary Project team, with whom I have enjoyed sharing and playing so many games. Thank heavens no one ever saw us!

Sue Stalley for her belief in Circle Time with children with severe and moderate learning difficulties, and for the outrageously camp game of 'Twinkle Twinkle'.

And thanks too, to all the countless other teachers who have bravely put up their hand on training days and said, 'I know a good game' and then found themselves sitting on a stranger's lap or crossing the room like a terrapin!

Thanks too to Jo, my patient editor, and Liam, her assistant. It can't have been easy!

Thank you *all*!

And thanks, too, to my husband Dennis and my children, Katie, Sophie, Lotte and Tom, for being so patient with the time it has taken to write this book and in showing me how to operate this wretched computer. Thank ◆❺▲↕⑥ (whoops) you!

1 How to use this book

I have been teaching for twenty-two years. During that time I seem to have heard about nothing but 'shortages'. We have had shortages of teachers, shortages of jobs, shortages of space; shortages of paper, books, computers, lunchtime supervisors, speech therapists, educational psychologists and headteachers; even, in rural areas, shortages of pupils; and always, *always*, shortages of cash. In the last few years, a whole new area of shortage has appeared. We now have an acute shortage of time.

This last shortage is painful. For whilst we have a deep obligation to our pupils to teach them to be literate and numerate, we also know we must not rush them through their childhood in a maelstrom of **doing** and a desert totally lacking in quiet, considered reflection.

Many teachers have found that Quality Circle Time provides a structured, organised, even scripted, time in the school week when children can consider aspects of their relationships as well as reflect upon their behaviour – where they can be honest about their difficulties and own the solutions to those difficulties.

However, with the advent of the Literacy Hour, and more 'hours' promised, many teachers are anxious that there will be little time left for Circle Time. They feel that to abandon Circle Time would be to fail the children. For it is through Quality Circle Time that children can learn how to isolate a problem, analyse it and then devise a collectively conceived and collectively owned solution.

What is more, Circle Time can be used to discuss and resolve problems with the curriculum as well as problems with friendships and relationships. A Circle Time spent discussing 'I find doing my sums difficult when …' can help a teacher become much clearer about her teaching of number work.

So how can teachers be sure that they will be able to accommodate all the demands of the timetable and still retain Circle Time?

One way is to forge a link between Circle Time and the curriculum. That is the purpose of this book.

In this book I offer a collection of poems that I have written which can be read during the Literacy Hour. They are also suitable for use as prompts for discussion during the weekly Circle Time.

The poems are concerned with missing Mum, making new friends, listening in class, feeling cross and in a temper and many other subjects – all of which it is important to discuss with children at either Key Stage One or Two.

So how would this work?

1. Use the poem during the Literacy Hour

- The poems can be read first during the Literacy Hour.
- They can be read together and they can be discussed in groups.
- They can be photocopied onto acetates and shown to the whole class on the OHP.
- They are simple and metrical, and have rhyme schemes designed to help children learn them by heart if necessary.
- They were written taking into account the recommendations for the range of poetry to be used with Key Stage One and Two pupils in the National Literacy Strategy framework.
- During the Literacy Hour the children can learn to pull out the meaning of a poem, and find out that it is important to discover the author's intentions when writing the poem. Questions to be asked include the following:

  'Why do you think the author wrote this poem?'
  'How is the little boy in this poem feeling?'
  'How do we know this?'
  'What are some of the words used in this poem that show us how he is feeling?'

- During the Literacy Hour there need be no significant discussion about how the children *themselves* would feel if they were in the same situation as a child in a poem. That can be saved for Circle Time.

○ This means that children can, even when quite small, learn to discuss a story – albeit it one in verse – objectively. Of course, they won't be able to do this straightaway in Reception, but the intention is there. By the time they get to the end of that key stage they will have the beginnings of a critical mind.

2. Use the same *poem* as the theme for the weekly Circle Time

○ Later in the week, during Circle Time, the children can use the poem and the insights they have gained from studying it to start a Circle Time discussion.

○ The children will not need to have the poem explained again – although it will be important either to re-read it together or to read it to them again. They will already have grasped the meaning of the poem during the Literacy Hour. This means that you can have an informed discussion in Circle Time, getting quickly to the heart of the subject.

○ In order to facilitate a purposeful and disciplined Circle Time that will not waffle on forever or go round and round in a terrifyingly tedious way I have recommended the use of a **Circle Time script**.

○ Each poem comes with suggestions for a specific script. These you may use, or not, as you feel appropriate! Instructions about using the scripts will be found in the next chapter.

In summary, you should remember to do the following:

- **Discuss the poems, as poetry, during the Literacy Hour.**
- **Discuss the** themes **raised by the poems during Circle Time.**

To reinforce a point, it is important to discuss the poem before bringing it to Circle Time.

I am not suggesting that all of your Circle Times are to be prompted by a poem, nor am I suggesting that all of your work during the Literacy Hour will be transferable to a Circle Time. But given that we do live with an awful time shortage, it would seem to be a good idea to use materials that can efficiently reinforce each other across the curriculum.

Support staff, educational psychologists, speech therapists and other outside agencies

If you have anyone from an outside agency coming in to work with your class or with an individual pupil, you can choose a *relevant* poem to discuss during the Literacy Hour.

You can then encourage the support teacher, or whoever, to use the same theme and poem for a Circle Time in order to discuss the issues that concern her and the child, or class, she has come in to see. This means that the person coming in from the outside is able not only to discuss the problem with a class or child who has already looked at the problem, but also – despite being an outside agency – to reinforce your curriculum work.

This helps the person coming in, because they know that the topic is already alive in your classroom. If they then ask you to follow up their work throughout the week, you can put this on the Circle Time script as a **target**.

Meeting this target will not be an irritating extra chore, robbing you of even more time, but a reinforcement of the discussions you have already had with the class, first during the Literacy Hour and then with the support teacher during a Circle Time.

If they have come in to see one specific child, a Circle Time for the whole class, with everyone making helpful suggestions for the child concerned, can be very beneficial. See *Effective IEPs through Circle Time* by Margaret Goldthorpe, published by LDA, 1998 (for address see page 86).

All in all, we are looking at the following:

- ◗ One part of the curriculum reinforcing another.
- ◗ Maintaining a valuable part of our week, Circle Time, despite time pressures.
- ◗ Finding ways of making the work of others in our classroom relevant to the rest of the work done throughout the week.

And, as each poem comes with a 'ready meal', a pre-planned Circle Time, it will help save teachers valuable planning time. It might even help you to get home in the light occasionally.

2 Circle Time

or

is there a Delia Smith in the house?

There are as many recipes for Circle Time as there are for Christmas cake. Like cakes, some of these seem splendid affairs, full of nuts and fruit and fancy seeds, but they cook up like bricks. Others appear to be simple and sophisticated, but when you come to taste them the result is simple, and it's also rather boring!

In an effort to improve matters, you may decide to borrow a recipe from a friend who seems to turn out brilliant results time after time; but when you try her recipe you end up with an awful old pudding, not the original, tasty creation you had in mind.

Often our Circle Times can seem like that. We know everyone else is doing Circle Time and in the staff room colleagues tell us all about their fabulous results – about the hilarious games and the heartstopping moments of mutual assistance and understanding shared between them and the children.

And we think of our own efforts: a quick game of 'Fruit Salad'; a round of 'What I have enjoyed this week'; a sharp 'Don't tilt your chair or you'll fall backwards and go blind'; pass the bells; then up off the carpet and out to play. That's all OK in its way, but it's hardly the life-enhancing weekly experience that the NQT with the Monsoon frock and the ethnic rucksack is always going on about.

At moments like this what we need is a *guaranteed* recipe – one which, whilst we don't always *have* to use it, will never let us down. If inspiration fails, we can be sure this won't.

We need Delia Smith!

When I first found the Jenny Mosley Quality Circle Time Model I felt many of my problems were solved. The integral Circle Time scripts will take us through most situations we will meet in a Circle Time and lead us to a result where we have a group of children who have together shared a problem, owned the problem and devised a mutually agreed, owned solution.

I had found a Christmas cake recipe I could depend upon!

There are some really important ingredients in this mixture, and these are the ground rules:

1. When having a round with a speaking object, only the person holding the object may speak. This rule holds good for the teacher too. If you must speak, you will have to get up, cross the circle, touch the object and say, 'Sorry to interrupt, but I just need to mention ...' before saying whatever it is that is so important.
2. There are to be no put-downs or 'pointy' laughter during the Circle Time.
3. No one may mention anyone else by name in a negative way. This is so that the children will learn to criticise the **behaviour** they don't like, not the **child** involved.
4. If you do not wish to make a contribution, you may say 'Pass'.
5. This is a rule for you. It's a hard rule, but if you don't keep it you will really shoot yourself in the foot.

   You must never say negative things to anyone at any time during the Circle Time.

There, I've said it! And I can hear you saying, 'Oh, come on!' But it's absolutely crucial.

If you find you are confronted with undesirable behaviour, giggling, slouching or catching one another's eye, it is better to use the technique of **adjacent praise** than to criticise.

This means saying to a child who is behaving well and is near the child wriggling about, or whatever, 'Well done, I like the way you are sitting up straight and listening.'

Now, you have to believe me about this, but I can promise you that the child who is wriggling will, even if only momentarily, sit up. At this point you should not waste a nano-second before looking at the wriggler and saying clearly, 'Well done, now you are sitting up beautifully too. Thank you.'

And smile. Really smile!

I have never known this to fail, even with very difficult year 7 children. The secret is in praising the miscreant instantly, however slight the improvement. They will look surprised, but they will have done what you wanted without being directly confronted, and you won't have spoiled the atmosphere.

Another way to deal with this situation is to say, 'I can see lots of lovely listening/good eye contact/sitting up straight ...' – whatever you want – 'over on this side of the circle. Now I can see it here and here. Goodness me, I think everyone is now listening. Aren't you wonderful.' They will be.

These are only little tricks but they do work and they are so much less depressing than bawling, 'Will you shut up and listen.' After that no one feels wonderful – least of all you.

If someone really won't stop being silly, I find it helps to say, 'I am sorry, but if you do that again you must miss the next game.' If they do it again, immediately play a favourite, fast game. Then go back to the Circle Time. This also works well. Believe me!

Now let us look at a script.

The theme of the Circle Time

Before you do anything you must be sure you know *why* you are holding a Circle Time. 'Because it's on the timetable' is not an acceptable answer!

In any Circle Time you need to be able to answer the question, 'What is the purpose of this Circle Time?' That is to say, what is the agenda for this Circle Time?

If you are using a poem from this book, you have the agenda already in place. As we have seen, the poem that you have read during the Literacy Hour can provide you with the agenda for your weekly Circle Time. The script offered in this book can provide the format.

The subject might be falling out with a friend, missing Mum or the death of a pet. Whatever it is, it is important to tell the children exactly why they are having a Circle Time.

For example, if you are looking at the poem about the death of the gerbil (page 37), you might say, 'Do you remember the poem we read this week about the gerbil who died from kindness and eating solid glue? Well, this week we are going to talk about Ravi's idea of having a class pet and what that might mean for each of us.'

Never forget to keep the children informed about the purpose of a Circle Time. School isn't a guessing game!

The script

Read poem

Opening game

- Playing games helps to pull the group together and provide lots of initial enjoyment. Children will come to love Circle Time and want to use it to tackle their difficulties.
- One way to encourage this to happen quickly is to make sure things get off to a good start with a lot of controlled fun.
- But these games have a lot more to offer than just good fun (although fun is important!). They are also there to improve the skills the children need to become good problem solvers.
- So there are games to improve:
  - mutual trust,
  - self-esteem,
  - speaking and listening skills,
  - co-operation,
  - negotiation skills.

- Be sure to tell the children why they are playing each game and what skill the game helps to foster. If the children know why they are doing an activity, they will learn from it much more quickly than if they just play it for its own sake. Just as we don't do Circle Time 'because it's on the timetable', so we don't play games just because they are in the book.
- It helps if you choose a game that will reinforce the theme of the Circle Time. For example, if you are trying to encourage better co-operation between the children, you might play a game that encourages a better understanding of how good it feels to co-operate.
- Each of the prompt scripts in this book has at least two games included in it.
- Try to play an initial game that moves the children around. If they spend the whole Circle Time next to their best friend, they will not think as creatively or be as open to new ideas as they will if they are sitting next to a child they do not know so well.

- Saying, 'Stand up and cross the circle if [for example] you like classical music' will teach them not to be frightened to hold opinions that may not be widely shared.

Opening round

- This is the round in which you set out the theme of the Circle Time and each child has a chance to say how they feel about the subject under discussion.
- Once the agenda is settled, each person in the circle has the opportunity to make a contribution to an initial exploration of the issue.
- We make sure this happens by having a **conch** or **speaking object** to pass round from child to child. You may speak only when you are holding the speaking object.
- You can use a soft toy, a small teddy bear, a papier maché or alabaster egg from Oxfam Trading or any object that fits comfortably in the hand of a child and has significance to the class.
- It is a really good idea to give the children the opening part of a sentence you wish them to finish, for example:

  'I find it difficult to listen in class when …',
  'I am happy at playtime when …', or
  'Sometimes I feel sad at school when …'

  This helps the shyer children to get started. It also means that younger children, who don't always know quite what is being asked of them, have got a lead.

- With Nursery and Reception class children, it can help enormously if you have a puppet or soft toy for them to speak to. For example, after reading the poem 'I don't feel very well, Mum' (page 30), you might pass round a small furry hedgehog and say to the children, 'Tell Harry Hedgehog what makes you feel sad at lunchtime. Say to him, "I feel really sad at lunchtime when …" '.
- Or you might ask the children to tell Harry what makes him upset. You might say, after reading 'Now I'm in trouble too!' (page 34), 'Harry Hedgehog sometimes gets really angry. Tell

him what you think makes him really cross in the playground. Start the sentence with, "I think you get cross in the playground when …" '.

- Children do not have to speak and can say, 'Pass', but I think it helps them to speak if you ask them to say the opening part of the sentence. Even if they cannot finish the sentence, at least they have spoken and heard their own voice. What is more, the rest of the class have heard them. It is also the case that sometimes, having started a sentence, a child finds they can finish it.

Open Forum

- This is a *brief* time in which to discuss the issue freely – for five or six minutes, at most.
- Make sure the children raise their hands before speaking. It is a good idea to try to teach children, from as young an age as possible, to lower their hand whilst someone else is speaking and raise it again when they have finished. This can help them to learn to listen to the person speaking rather than concentrating on remembering what it is they are going to say when their hand is 'answered'.
- To start a discussion, try to ask a few 'open-ended' questions.

Would it help if …?

- At this point you can ask the children if they can think of anything that might help with the problem they have been talking about.
- I usually say, 'Let's take twenty seconds to think about something we might do that would help.'
- Then pass the speaking object round again and ask the children to start the sentence with, 'Would it help if …'.
- If any child cannot think of anything to say that is not a problem, they can say, 'Pass'.
- At the end of the round, I say, 'Let's go round again. This time you say which of the suggestions made you liked the best.' This gives everyone a chance to feel they have had a

hand in the problem-solving process. Everyone feels attached to at least one solution. They can own a suggestion even if they were unable to make one.

● How you deal with the suggestions made is up to you. You may like to select a few and suggest you all try them, or you might say, 'What very clever children you are to think of such good ideas! Let's try to remember these good suggestions for when we have the problem.'

● I would suggest that you write all of the suggestions down on the back of the script. You may only choose two or three as targets now, but you might like to use some of the other suggestions at a later date and it would be a pity if you could not remember them.

● It can help to record them in a visual way – it helps to make an abstract idea concrete. You may want to put a target up on the wall in a pictorial form.

● It is very important to be aware that very young children may not have many ideas for solving their own problems; indeed they may on occasion have none. Do not despair. You may have to lead them to ideas during the Open Forum. If you help them now, whilst they are still quite small and new to school, by introducing them to some good strategies for managing their own behaviour and then getting them to own them through the round, 'Say which suggestion you liked the best', they will gradually build up a bank of ideas which they can call upon.

● In addition, they will begin to see themselves as problem solvers.

Select two or three suggestions as targets for the week

● Once you have a good collection of helpful suggestions on the back of your Circle Time script (or wherever you choose to record them), you will need to choose one or two as targets.

● These are the suggestions you are going to follow through and work at with the class throughout the week.

○   You will need concrete ways of displaying these targets to the class and also concrete ways of both encouraging and recording success.

Some practical ways to celebrate achievement and record success are offered below.

A praise tree

You could have a representation of an oak tree with the target written in gold above it. Every time the children achieve a specific target decided on in Circle Time, they could put a golden leaf on the oak tree. You could explain this to the class as follows:

> **'Every time [for example] you manage to be quiet while I tell you what you are going to be doing during this lesson, you may go and get a leaf and put it on the tree with a drawing pin.'**

This provides the children with a concrete representation of the abstract notion 'success'.

Posters

Another way of recording successes is to use LDA's undersea poster with reusable sticky fishes. You can use it in the same way as you used the tree; children can stick a fish on the undersea picture every time the particular target chosen is met. There is another, equally useful, poster: of the night sky, with reusable stick-on stars. The advantage of the LDA reusable pictures is that you can grab one from the stock cupboard and get on with using it as soon as you decide you need it, without having to spend hours cutting out trees, leaves, fishes or stars.

School praise tree

A praise tree could be placed in a central position in the school. The whole school could have a Circle Time about a particular issue, all reading the same poem during Literacy Hour, and then focusing on a particular target.

This would help the whole school to gain a sense of collective pride. Visitors to the school would be able to appreciate all the acts of kindness, or whatever has been chosen, being celebrated.

Clear and precise stickers

Stickers can turn children into message boards of their own success – but only if they are really specific.

Make sure that you note children's success with their Circle Time targets, using the right sticker for the job. If you are encouraging children not to get cross with each other in the classroom, for example, you need a sticker that says, 'Thank you for staying calm.'

There are lots of stickers on the market. LDA produce some very good ones which are designed to support the Quality Circle Time Model.

Spoken praise

The most effective motivator of all is clear, specific praise delivered with a big, warm smile. Catch them getting it right, give a big smile and a 'Well done.'

Photocopiable ideas by Jenny Mosley

Jenny Mosley's book of photocopiable materials includes dozens of ways of recording success with targets and is very useful. This is available from the address in the Resources section at the back of the book (page 92).

More ideas

My book *Effective IEPs through Circle Time*, published by LDA, has a chapter on rewards, incentives and celebrating success.

Celebration of achievement

There is a section in the Quality Circle Time script which calls for celebration of achievement. This is without doubt as important as anything else you are going to do in the Circle Time, and possibly as important as anything else you do all week.

As teachers or parents, we know how important it is to say, 'Thank you' and 'Well done', even for the smallest thing that a child has done that we want them to do. Saying, 'Well done! That's four words in a row in proper cursive script. Excellent! Now let's have a crack at five!' is going to get you a great deal more joined-up writing than saying, 'Four words! Just four words! What use is that? Now go away and do it properly.' That will get you nowhere.

Occasionally teachers say to me, 'Why should I thank them, or praise them, or reward them, for things they should be doing anyway?' I wish I could say that I heard that rarely, but sadly that is not so.

How do you answer that kind of question? By saying, 'Give up now. Somewhere through the years you've lost the plot'?

I think, rather, you have to be aware that maybe whoever said it has not been thanked enough themselves. Maybe you could help, either by thanking them more or by noticing things that can be praised – for example, 'My class loved your assembly, Mrs Richards. They'd like me to thank you.' You may be met by a hostile glance or even be cut dead, but press on. Remember, if you get a negative response, the child who scribbles on their drawing when you say it is good. You have to press on, praising where it's due, whatever the reaction.

It is also very important to consider having regular staff Circle Times run according to the Quality Circle Time script. They would give increased time and space for adults to be able to thank and praise each other.

So, what might you say during the section called **Celebration of achievement**?

- It is a good point at which to thank five or six children for things they have done that week: 'Thank you for the five words of cursive script, Vinit.' 'Thank you for the lovely smile I was met with this morning, Darren.' 'Thank you for being such a good register monitor this week, Stacey.'
- Try to remember to thank everyone in the class for something during each half term. If necessary, keep notes. It will only take ten or twenty seconds to say four or five 'thank yous', but it will pay huge dividends.
- Ask if anyone in the group would like to thank anyone else for a kind deed, word or thought they have shown in the week. They will, and the people they thank will probably be a surprise to you.
- This is also a good time for giving out the rewards achieved for successful completion of previously agreed targets. These may be targets from a previous Circle Time, or they may be targets from an IEP, or they may be learning targets. Whatever they are, if there is cause to celebrate achievement, do it in front of the whole class and get the maximum effect for someone's self-esteem.
- Remember that these rewards can be from child to child as well as from teacher to pupil.

Closing game

- The Circle Time usually finishes with another game. This time it should be one which calms people down, and maybe encourages them to thank each other and notice the successes they have had during the Circle Time.
- Like the opening game, it usually has some connection with the theme of the Circle Time. However, this may be a good time to reward a hard-working circle with their favourite game – no matter what its theme is!

Organisation of the scripts and poems

- You may find it helpful to keep a Circle Time file (a ring binder or similar type of file) in which to store your scripts, accompanying photocopies and OHP sheets of the poems.
- Photocopy a blank Quality Circle Time script in readiness for each week. There is a photocopy master later in this chapter (see page 19).
- Date the script for the week.
- Fill in the Circle Time theme.
- If you are using one of the poems, fill in the title of the poem and the page on which it appears.
- Once you have settled upon the theme, fill in the names of the opening and closing games. Try to find appropriate games.
- Write in the opening sentence. Make sure it is as open ended as possible.
- Take the script into Circle Time with you and put it near you so you can look at it when you need to. Have a pen to hand.
- Show the children the script so they become familiar with it and begin to know their way round it.
- Keep notes of good suggestions made during the 'Would it help ...' round on the *back* of the script.
- Note on the script the targets for the week so you can remind both yourself and the children of them and also so you gain a good idea of the progress made by the children over the year.

- File each script in a ring binder so you remember all the good ideas and also have a record of topics you have covered and how the children handled the problems.
- This file will prove invaluable for next year's planning.
- You can follow this procedure for any Circle Time, not just the ones using the poems.
- You can use some poems several times. Many of them have more than one theme.
- You may want to photocopy the contents of the file and pass them to the teacher who will be taking the class the next year, so she can see the work done by the children and the topics which have had at least an initial airing.
- The games that are provided can all be used for other Circle Times. Your file will become a useful bank of ideas.
- Please remember that you don't have to use the Circle Time scripts in the book. They are there as prompts and to help with ideas. They are not the only way of tackling each topic.
- The age range suggested at the top of each script is for the script, not the poem. The poems can be read to children of any age you think appropriate.
- You may want to produce a booklet for each child so they too have all the Circle Time suggestions.

Example (front)

DATE:	YEAR:	*4*
POEM READ DURING THE LITERACY HOUR: *'For what we are about to receive …'*	**THEME OF TODAY'S CIRCLE TIME:** *Healthy eating*	

CIRCLE TIME SCRIPT

READ POEM

OPENING GAME

Cross the circle if … you have laces in your shoes/you live in a flat/you like the Spice Girls/you like playing football/you like eating fruit/you hate vegetables/you love vegetables etc.

OPENING ROUND
[The beginning of the sentence]

'I think it's probably good for me to eat …'

OPEN FORUM

Encourage a discussion about the food we like to eat, what is good for us and the problems of a mismatch.

WOULD IT HELP IF …
[Write good suggestions on the back of this script]

To start this, recap their ideas about what was good to eat.

SELECT TWO OR THREE SUGGESTIONS AS TARGETS FOR THE WEEK
[Write them here]

Sam's, Vinit's and Justin's

CELEBRATION OF ACHIEVEMENT

CLOSING GAME

Pass the thunder, Pass the rain.
Finish with 'Thank you' and 'Bon appetit!'

Their suggestions (back)

Sam: Would it help if we ate one thing each day which we knew was good for us?

Elaine: Would it help if we banned crisps at break time and brought in fruit instead?

Katie: Would it help if we didn't have batter on the school fish?

Charlotte: Would it help if we only had buns for dessert once a week?

Preeti: Would it help if we asked the school cooks to a Circle Time so they can talk to us about how difficult it is to do the lunches?

Tom: Would it help if we had oven chips instead of fried chips?

Vinit: Would it help if we took more exercise at home?

Melanie: Would it help if we had salad twice a week even in the winter?

Justin: Would it help if sometimes we had the school dinner vegetables raw?

There is a blank script on the following page for you to photocopy and use.

DATE:	YEAR:
POEM READ DURING THE LITERACY HOUR:	THEME OF TODAY'S CIRCLE TIME:

CIRCLE TIME SCRIPT

READ POEM

OPENING GAME

OPENING ROUND
[The beginning of the sentence]

OPEN FORUM

WOULD IT HELP IF ...
[Write good suggestions on the back of this script]

SELECT TWO OR THREE SUGGESTIONS AS TARGETS FOR THE WEEK
[Write them here]

CELEBRATION OF ACHIEVEMENTS

CLOSING GAME

3 The poems

Morning school

I'm peering through the window,
Waving Mum goodbye.
I feel so very sad it hurts.
I can't help it if I cry.

Mum's turning round and waving,
She's smiling at me too,
Blowing lots of kisses,
Saying, 'See you soon!'

I can't help it that I cry so hard
When it's time for school to start.
I can't bear to see her walk away,
It really breaks my heart.

My teacher comes and picks me up
And kisses my wet face,
Saying, 'Let's get the Play-Doh out.
Come on, let's have a race!'

Soon we're making models,
Me and my friend Sue,
We're mucking about with paper
And paint, and sticky glue.

When at last it's home time
And Mummy's face appears,
I'm laughing with my teacher,
I've forgotten all those tears.

Book corner

I smile at my friend
And I say, 'Let's share.
Come and sit beside me,
Here on this chair.
Come and sit beside me,
And let us take a look,
Sitting side by side,
Sharing pictures in this book.'

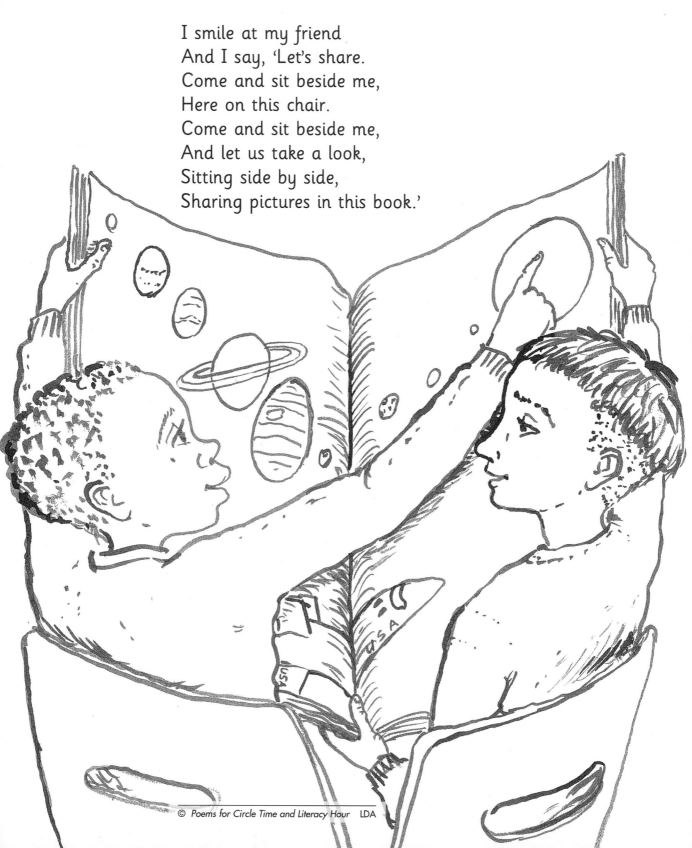

Dressing-up box

I like *that* hat,
And I want *that* hat,
And I think I'll have the other one too.

But perhaps it would be kind,
And I really do not mind,
If I share these hats with you.

Put your hand up!

When I know the answer,
And I'm really sure I do,
I put my hand up nice and straight,
So I can tell you too.
I don't shout out or holler,
I don't do that, no fear!
I just put my hand up
Until my teacher says, 'Yes, dear?'

The Lego pencil

I've got a Lego pencil,
It came from Legoland.
It's got a rubber on the top,
And a yellow Lego band.

I know you'd like to borrow it,
And I'm sure that's quite OK.
But please be sure to give it back
Before it's time for play.

Story time

I'm sitting on the carpet,
Somewhere near the door.
The sun is shining through the blinds,
Making patterns on the floor.

I know that I must listen
To the story being told,
But it's very hard to listen,
When the carpet's turning gold.

Who's a bully?

Move up, silly, *I'm* sitting there.
I said, 'Go away', this is *my* chair.
Put that crayon down, it's *my* blue,
I don't care if you want it too.

Give that back, it's *my* clockwork mouse.
No, you can't play in the Wendy House.
If you won't go, I'll push you out.
You still won't go? Well, I'll have to shout.

Get out now, or I'll kick your shin,
I'm going to choose who comes in.
Don't be a baby, I only pushed a bit.
Clear off now – Ow! Don't hit!

Why is Miss looking so mad,
Saying some children are making her sad?
She says some people aren't being fair.
I expect she means *you*. Get off, that's *my* chair.

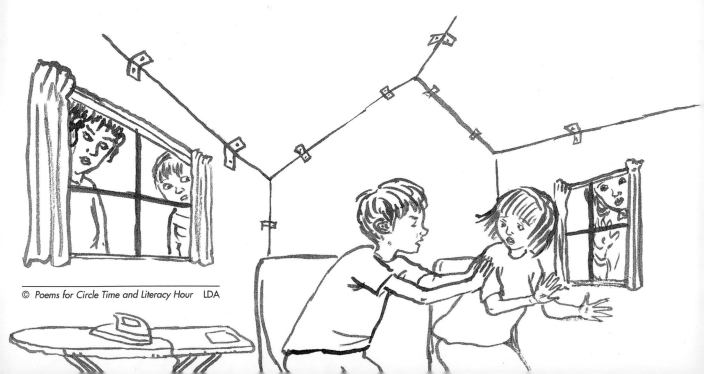

Friends

I'm not friends with Tom today,
And he's not friends with me.
He says that he likes Justin best,
And he's asked him round to tea.

So I walked about the playground,
Pretending I could fly,
But I fell and hurt my elbow
And had a little cry.

The dinner lady picked me up
Saying, 'Come along with me,
He'll be friends with you tomorrow,
Just you wait and see.'

I don't feel very well, Mum

I've got a headache and a tummyache
And I want to stay at home.
My mummy will be here today
So I wouldn't be alone.

But Mum says, 'You must go to school,
Your tummy's not that bad.'
But I know it isn't just the pain,
That's making me feel sad.

I miss my mum at lunchtime,
When the big boys pick on me,
And I wish it was *my* mum outside,
With her blue mug full of tea.

I wish my mum was with me
When the afternoon is long,
And I can't remember all the words
To our assembly song.

So I've got a headache and a tummyache
And I want to stay in bed.
But I know that I will go to school,
With some medicine for my head.

My mum gives me a cuddle,
And a really lovely hug,
And says she'll still be here tonight,
Drinking tea from her blue mug.

New friend

I'm standing in the playground,
And I'm standing all alone,
My only friend's away today.
I think she's ill at home.

I'm feeling very lonely
And I think that I might cry.
I'd really like to play with you,
But I know I'm much too shy.

Perhaps I'll just stand near you,
And maybe ask your name,
And if you smile and talk to me
Perhaps we'll play a game.

I'm running in the playground,
I'm playing 'It' with Jo.
I think I've got a new friend now,
I'm glad I said, 'Hello'.

Questions, questions, questions!

Why is my lunch horrid
When yours is really scrummy?
Why must I be here at school
When I want to be with Mummy?
Why do all the other boys
Play football with each other?
Why have I got a sister
When I really need a brother?
Why is reading difficult
For me but not for you?
Why is your school jumper cool
And mine's just navy blue?
School's so full of questions
That go with all our tasks,
But the hardest ones to answer
Are the ones I'm scared to ask.

Goalie gloves

Darren's got some goalie gloves,
They're black and navy blue.
I wish that I had gloves like that,
And could be a goalie too.

Craig has got a baseball glove,
He brought it in to school.
It's not a real leather glove
But I think it's really cool.

I have to wear green woolly gloves,
They're on elastic string.
They might not be such special gloves –
But only mine go PING!

Now I'm in trouble too!

Why do those naughty boys always pick on *me*?
It makes me really furious and if I cried, they'd see.
They never pick on Thomas and they never pick
    on Jack.
My mum says that's because *they* don't get
    angry back.

She says that I have got to learn to simply walk away,
And not look wild or angry, just go away and play.
But I hate it when they pick on me, it makes me
    really cross
When they laugh at me and call me names to show
    me they're the boss.

But fighting back is hopeless, I just get told off too.
So when those big boys pick on me – please, may I
    play with you?

Eczema

I've got eczema and it itches
And it hurts behind my knees.
Some children in my class at school
Just laugh at me and tease.

But *they* don't know how bad it feels
When your fingers crack and bleed,
And your elbows hurt so very much
You can't think straight enough to read.

When I sit there in assembly
And I itch so much I scratch it,
The nasty children laugh at me
Saying, 'Don't talk to her, you'll catch it.'

Why can't they understand that
It's not my fault, I'm just unlucky?
It's something I was born with,
I'm not 'Sad', 'Unclean' or 'Yucky'.

Why can't they say, 'Poor Rachel,
Her eczema's bad today.
Let's cheer her up and make her laugh,
See if she'd like to play.'

In your dreams

My dad's a famous footballer,
He even knows Paul Ince.
He lives at home with me and Mum,
And a Doberman called Prince.

Yeah, he lives at home with me and Mum,
I see him every day.
On Saturdays he takes me out
To see the Arsenal play.

He's got a Harley-Davidson
And his Lamborghini's blue,
He let's me use his mobile phone.
He's getting me one too.

And he's going to get us Sky TV,
We'll watch football every night.
And he's taking us all to Florida,
To Disneyland, that's right!

It's true, it's true, it's really true,
I'm telling you it's true!
And he lives at home with me and Mum.
Oh, please, let that be true.

The gerbil

Oh! I can see the gerbil!
I can see its little face.
It isn't in its wooden cage,
It's by the new bookcase.

I have a horrid feeling
That it shouldn't look like that.
It's rather still and quiet,
It should be running on that mat.

I really liked that gerbil.
I think it liked me too.
I used to feed it spelling books
And bits of solid glue.

I don't think I will ever feel
That silky, soft, small head
Snuggling up my jumper sleeve,
I think that gerbil's dead.

Oh I *really* liked that gerbil,
But what makes me want to weep
Is knowing that it loved me too,
Perhaps it's just asleep?

For what we are about to receive ...

We have a very healthy life,
My family and me.
We eat a lot of vegetables
And wholemeal bread for tea.

I know it's very good for me
And I'll grow up tall and clever,
And Mum says that she hopes her skin
Will stay young and soft forever.

But at school I choose the greasy chips
And soft fish fingers too,
And I love the pink and sticky buns
And the sauce that's just red goo!

So I'll go on eating vegetables
And lentil bake, for Mum,
But my best day is Thursday,
'Cos it's burgers in a bun!

Complacency

Last year we all teased Robert,
We kept him out of our games,
We picked on him in the playground
And we muttered nasty names.

It really was such brilliant fun!
The teachers didn't fuss.
When he said he was unhappy
They said *he* was horrid to *us*!

The teachers didn't see us
Laughing at Robert's hair,
Or leaving him out of the football.
Perhaps they didn't care!

Robert grew quite angry,
They called his behaviour 'bad'.
Nobody noticed that Robert
Was being driven mad.

By the hurtful, mocking glances
From our cosy little clique.
We didn't know how strong we were
But we knew that Rob was weak.

We all find school so easy,
We're articulate, clever and clean,
And our mums all hear our reading,
They never think we're mean.

So last year we all teased Robert,
Our clever, confident crew,
Until he left the school in misery –
So this year, we'll all tease you.

© *Poems for Circle Time and Literacy Hour*   LDA

School trip

Oh YES!! We're on our way,
We're off on our school trip!
We're going to see the Children's Farm.
There's a donkey there called Pip.

We'll be on this coach an hour or so,
And we're not allowed to shout,
Or sing too loud or fight at all,
Or swear or run about.

We did a lot of sheets this week
About the animals we'll see,
The goats and ducks and chickens,
How we mustn't set them free.

And we saw a load of photos
Of the animals who live there,
There's a creature called a Jacob sheep
Who has tons of thick brown hair.

And we mustn't feed the duck
Or stick Doritos down her beak,
Or give her Coca Cola
Like the other group did last week.

And no one's to nick the rabbits
Or put chicks into their pocket.
A boy did that from Miss Mitchell's class.
Wow! Did she give him a rocket!

But the best bit will be the picnic lunch,
I've eaten most of mine.
I drank my drink in the car park
And my KitKat was gone by nine.

But I've got some fish-paste sandwiches,
And half a banana too.
I think that Pip will really like those.
Do you think that ducks can chew?

Playing with fire

Leanne says that Ricky smells,
Leanne sees Amit cry and tells,
Leanne says we hate Sean as well.
I think she's cool, Leanne.

Leanne says that we're the best,
It's great to laugh at all the rest.
Leanne says, 'They're such a pest.'
But I am friends with Leanne.

Leanne thinks that school is dumb,
And often doesn't even come.
I know she hasn't told her mum,
Who says, 'I am tired, Leanne.'

Leanne laughs behind her hand
At lots of things that she 'Can't stand',
Like my new shoes and blue hairband.
I'm sometimes scared of Leanne.

My mum says that I should find
A friend who thinks that being kind
Is really cool, and doesn't mind
If I'm not like Leanne.

4 The scripts

DATE:	
POEM READ DURING THE LITERACY HOUR: *'Morning school'*	**THEME OF TODAY'S CIRCLE TIME:** *Missing your mummy, but feeling happy* *as part of a class group*

CIRCLE TIME SCRIPT

READ POEM
Read 'Morning school' (page 22).

OPENING GAME

<u>CLAPPING NAMES:</u> *The children say the name of each child in the circle in turn. As they say the name, they clap the rhythm. (Older children can click fingers; those even older can do both!) This game helps everyone feel special.*

<u>CO-OPERATIVE LAPS:</u> *The group stands in a tightly packed circle, standing sideways to the centre of the circle. When you say, 'Sit', everyone sits on the lap of the person behind. Each person holds the waist of the person in front. If this is perfectly co-ordinated by the whole group no one will fall over.*

OPENING ROUND
[The beginning of the sentence]

Say that everyone feels 'wobbly' sometimes in the morning, even when they are quite big, and even when they have been at school for a long time.
'When it's time to come into school sometimes I feel ...'

OPEN FORUM

Encourage the children to discuss how they feel – if things get better when they get bigger, if it's worse if a sibling is staying at home, if there's something they aren't looking forward to at school. Lead into talking about what can help them feel better, introducing the idea that they may feel better if they have lots of friends and some nice things to do.

WOULD IT HELP IF ...
[Write good suggestions on the back of this script]

SELECT TWO OR THREE SUGGESTIONS AS TARGETS FOR THE WEEK
[Write these here]

CELEBRATION OF ACHIEVEMENT

CLOSING GAME

<u>I'M FEELING HAPPY BUT I JUST CAN'T SMILE:</u> *The children go round the circle one at a time saying this to the person next to them. Tell them to 'mug' a straight face. They will almost certainly have to laugh.*

<u>THANK YOU:</u> *Finish by asking them to say, 'Thank you' to the person next to them and then let the whole class applaud itself for a good Circle Time. (Group building!)*

DATE:	YEAR: _R/1/2_
POEM READ DURING THE LITERACY HOUR: *'Book corner'*	**THEME OF TODAY'S CIRCLE TIME:** *Sharing*

CIRCLE TIME SCRIPT

READ POEM
Read 'Book corner' (page 23).

OPENING GAME
CHANGE PLACES: *Tell children with something in common – for example, wearing a hairband, wearing a jumper – to change places. They could take turns to be the caller.*

MAGIC SWEETS: *Ask the first child to say to the one on their right that they have a bag of magic sweets. The second child chooses what kind they are. They then mime passing them round the circle and sharing them. Continue with another pair in the same way.*

OPENING ROUND
[The beginning of the sentence]

Tell the children to pass a teddy bear round and tell him something they would like to share with him (e.g. a game, food, sweets, bedtime story, the home corner). Each child says, 'Teddy, would you like to share my ....'.

OPEN FORUM
Tell the children to talk about all the things in the class that they can share (e.g. sand, books, Duplo, taped stories with two sets of headphones).

WOULD IT HELP IF ...
[Write good suggestions on the back of this script.]

Encourage each child to think of one thing they could try to share this week (e.g. 'Would it help if I shared the doll's pram?' Do not encourage them to make offers to specific people as they will tend to share with their best friends. The idea is that they will share with anyone.

SELECT TWO OR THREE SUGGESTIONS AS TARGETS FOR THE WEEK
[Write these here]

CELEBRATION OF ACHIEVEMENT

CLOSING GAME
PASS THE BELLS: *Explain that they are to pass the bells quietly from child to child.*

DATE:	
POEM READ DURING THE LITERACY HOUR: 'Dressing-up box'	**THEME OF TODAY'S CIRCLE TIME:** Sharing

CIRCLE TIME SCRIPT

READ POEM
Read 'Dressing-up box' (page 24).

OPENING GAME
TWINKLE, TWINKLE: This is like Fruit salad, but is adapted for very young children. Go round the circle, calling the first child 'Twinkle, Twinkle' and the next 'Little Star'; the third is 'Twinkle, Twinkle', the fourth 'Little Star' and so on round the circle. You then say, 'All the Twinkle, Twinkles stand up and run round and find a new seat.' Then ask all the Little Stars to stand up, run round and find a new seat. You should then have the children sitting next to people who are not their best friends.

OPENING ROUND
[The beginning of the sentence]
'When people want my things that I am playing with it makes me feel ...'
'When people won't let me share their things I feel ...'

OPEN FORUM
We can all discuss the different times and different activities that cause them to have problems with sharing.
Make a list together of the words you hear when people are not sharing: 'mine, don't snatch, push, kick, hit, go away, get out, leave it alone' and so on; and then make a list of words you hear when people are sharing: 'would you like, do you want, have some, yours, ours, turns, your turn, please, thank you'.
Discuss how to encourage one another to share.

WOULD IT HELP IF ...
[Write good suggestions on the back of this script]

SELECT TWO OR THREE SUGGESTIONS AS TARGETS FOR THE WEEK
[Write them here]

CELEBRATION OF ACHIEVEMENT

CLOSING GAME
PASS THE MIME: Ask one child to mime something (e.g. stroking a cat) and to pass the mime on to the next child in the circle. This child can carry on with the same mime (i.e. stroke the cat), adapt it (e.g. scratch its ears), or change the mime to something else. Go round until everyone – even you – has had a go.
THANK YOU: Finish by asking the children to say, 'Goodbye and thank you for sharing Circle Time' to the person on either side.

DATE:	YEAR: *1/2/3*
POEM READ DURING THE LITERACY HOUR: *'Put your hand up!'*	**THEME OF TODAY'S CIRCLE TIME:** *Classroom behaviour*

CIRCLE TIME SCRIPT

READ POEM
Read 'Put your hand up!' (page 25).

OPENING GAME

ANIMAL CRACKERS: *Like Fruit salad (see page 57) but with animals! Number the children round the circle: 1, 2, 3, 4, 1, 2, 3, 4. Tell them 1s are storks who cross the circle on one leg, 2s are humans who cross on two, 3s are monkeys who cross on two legs and an arm and 4s are horses who cross on all fours. Call out numbers. Once children are on different seats, stop.*

THE NOISY GAME: *Label the children A and B alternately. Tell the As they have to tell their partner, B, about their favourite hobby, food, pop group, football team etc. Explain at first the Bs do not listen. The Bs can make as much noise as they like, calling out to their friends or calling across the circle. Then you call for silence. Then the As talk to the Bs again; this time tell the Bs to listen very well, nodding their heads, smiling appropriately and so on. The children will discover that not only can you not hear if you don't listen but that there is no point in speaking if you are not being listened to.*

OPENING ROUND

Explain there are reasons for rules like knocking before going into a room, not interrupting, putting your hand up. Ask the children to think about what it would be like if we had no rules.
'I could make this classroom really noisy if I ...'   I could make this classroom really calm if I ...'

OPEN FORUM

Centre the discussion around how much work you would get done with rules and how much with no rules. How long Could they stand chaos, how they would feel (tired, headachy etc.). Some children may say it would be great. Remind them of the noisy game and what happened.

WOULD IT HELP IF ...
[Write good suggestions on the back of this script]

SELECT TWO OR THREE SUGGESTIONS AS TARGETS FOR THE WEEK
[Write them here]

CELEBRATION OF ACHIEVEMENT

CLOSING GAME

EYE CONTACT AND MOVE: *This is a silent game (phew!). Choose one child to start. They have to stand up and cross the circle, locking eyes with another child. As soon as that child realises it is they who is being looked at, they stand up and cross the circle, locking eyes with another child. The first child to walk across the circle sits in the seat vacated by the person they locked eyes with. The second child repeats the process.*

DATE: ....

POEM READ DURING THE LITERACY HOUR:	THEME OF TODAY'S CIRCLE TIME:
'The Lego pencil'	Lending and borrowing

CIRCLE TIME SCRIPT

READ POEM
Read 'The Lego pencil' (page 26).

OPENING GAME
WINK, WINK: Put one extra chair into the circle. Ask the child next to the empty chair to wink at someone on the other side of the circle. The person winked at crosses the circle in silence and sits in the empty chair. The person who now has the empty chair on their right winks at someone and they cross the circle and sit in the empty chair. Do this as fast as is sensible until the children are reasonably well muddled up.

WORDS: Have a brief round in which you say in turn a word that is associated with lending and borrowing (e.g. nick, break, take, keep, lose, damage, return, give back, remember, forget).

OPENING ROUND
[The beginning of the sentence]
You could start by saying lending and borrowing are a problem anywhere. Whilst we may have rules that discourage lending and borrowing, they will go on. We need to learn how to be sensible and reliable.
'I will lend things to other people if they ...'
'I don't like it when ...'

OPEN FORUM
Lead a general discussion about how people feel about lending and borrowing, including what helps them work and why they go wrong.
Remember that nobody is to be mentioned in a negative way.

WOULD IT HELP IF ...
[Write good suggestions on the back of this script]

SELECT TWO OR THREE SUGGESTIONS AS TARGETS FOR THE WEEK
[Write them here]

CELEBRATION OF ACHIEVEMENT

CLOSING GAME
PASS THE DRUM ROUND: Pass a drum to a child in the circle. They have to pass it on, pass the parcel style, until you strike the cymbals. Then the person holding the drum has to tap out the rhythm of a familiar tune and the rest try to guess it. Explain that they must put up their hand first, not call out. Children find it hard to pass the drum on, but they do learn not to try to cheat by hanging on to it.

DATE:	YEAR: *R or 1*
POEM READ DURING THE LITERACY HOUR: *'Story time'*	**THEME OF TODAY'S CIRCLE TIME:** *Listening and concentrating*

CIRCLE TIME SCRIPT

READ POEM
Read 'Story time' (page 27).

OPENING GAME
RAINBOW: *This is like Fruit salad (see page 57), but with colours. Assign colours to the children in turn. Call the colours out in random order. Once the children are all on different seats, stop.*

DUCK, DUCK, GOOSE: *Tell one child to stand and walk quickly round the outside of the circle, tapping each child gently on the shoulder and saying 'Duck' very quietly. Then they tap someone and say, 'Goose'. This child stands and the two run in opposite directions in order to try to reach the vacant chair first. The last to sit down starts the next round.*

OPENING ROUND
[The beginning of the sentence]

Talk to the children about how it is often difficult to listen and concentrate on what is being said in class. If the class is young, you can give them several examples of times when listening is hard (e.g. being distracted like the child in the poem; being tired, hot, sleepy, poorly; someone talking to them).
Give the group twenty seconds to think about what distracts them from listening.
'I find it hard to listen when …'   'I find it easier to listen when …'

OPEN FORUM
Continue the discussion, using the new information given by the children. Discuss their problems first, and then lead them into a discussion of solutions, using their ideas from 'I find it easier to listen when …'.

WOULD IT HELP IF …
[Write good suggestions on the back of this script]

SELECT TWO OR THREE SUGGESTIONS AS TARGETS FOR THE WEEK
[Write them here]

CELEBRATION OF ACHIEVEMENT

CLOSING GAME
CHINESE WHISPERS: *The first person whispers a sentence to the person on their right. The whisper is passed round the circle until it reaches the person to the immediate left of the one who started the round. This person says the sentence aloud, and the starter then says their sentence aloud to see how the two versions compare. Alternatively, stop after six children have had a go and ask for the sentence. Then get them to start a new sentence.*

TOUCH AND GO: *Tell one child to get up and tap another on the shoulder. The first child goes out. The second child taps a third on the shoulder and the second goes out, and so on. They may only tap someone who is sitting silently.*

DATE:	
POEM READ DURING THE LITERACY HOUR: *'Who's a bully?'*	**THEME OF TODAY'S CIRCLE TIME:** *Being rough with each other*

CIRCLE TIME SCRIPT

READ POEM
Read 'Who's a bully?' (page 28).

OPENING GAME
MY FRIENDS: *Choose one child to start. Take away their chair and explain that they should begin by saying,*
'I like all of my friends but especially those …' (wearing black shoes, wearing a school dress, who own a cat,
like doing sums, enjoy skipping etc.) Children in the category named cross the circle. The one who doesn't
get a chair chooses the next category, saying, 'I like all of my friends …' etc. After several children have had
a turn at choosing, put the missing chair back for the rest of Circle Time.

OPENING ROUND
Briefly remind the children about the child in the poem, who wouldn't let someone into the
Wendy House, wouldn't share the colours and pushed someone off a chair they had been sitting on.
Explain that this made another child upset and they had a fight.

[The beginning part of the sentence]
'I get upset and cross in class when people …'. Remind the children not to mention names.
'I feel happiest in class when …'

OPEN FORUM
Discuss whether the child in the poem could have behaved differently. Bring out the point that
at different times we are all unhappy, and squabble in the classroom because of that.
Talk about how they can make the classroom happier.

'WOULD IT HELP IF …'
[Write good suggestions on the back of this script]

SELECT TWO OR THREE SUGGESTIONS AS TARGETS FOR THE WEEK
[Write them here]

CELEBRATION OF ACHIEVEMENT
[Especially for kindness shown in the classroom]

CLOSING GAME
PASS THE THUNDER, PASS THE RAIN: *Either start the round yourself by making your fingers look like rain, or ask a child to*
start. The next person follows, then the next, until everyone is 'raining'. Then the first person pats their lap to represent
thunder. Continue round the circle. The first person says, 'Now the sun is coming out', and smiles at the next child.
The smile is passed round the circle.
THANKS: *Close by asking everyone to thank the person either side of them for a nice Circle Time.*

DATE:	YEAR: *R/1/2/3*
POEM READ DURING THE LITERACY HOUR: *'Friends'*	**THEME OF TODAY'S CIRCLE TIME:** *Falling out with our friends*

CIRCLE TIME SCRIPT

READ POEM
Read the poem 'Friends' (page 29).

OPENING GAME

<u>THROWING THE MAGIC NAME:</u> *The first child says the name of another child in the circle. As they say the name, they mime throwing a ball to the child whose name they have said, as if they are throwing the name. The child whose name it is mimes catching it. The second child then says the name of another child and mimes a throw at the same time. This results in children saying the names of children they don't often speak to.*

<u>CROSS THE CIRCLE IF ... :</u> *Tell the children to cross the circle if, for example, they have ever fallen out with friends, felt like crying because they have fallen out with their friends, think someone has taken their best friend away from them.*

OPENING ROUND
[The beginning of the sentence]

Pass a soft toy round as a speaking object and tell the children to tell the teddy (or whatever) how they feel when their friends won't play with them.

'When my friends are horrid to me I feel ...'   *'When I feel like this it makes me want to ...'*
The children will have only a limited range of responses; this is fine. The round is designed to show them that everyone feels lonely, sad or angry sometimes, not just them.

OPEN FORUM
Spend a few minutes bringing it to the children's attention that they have all said that their friends sometimes fall out with them and shut them out of groups or games. They also change best friends. These things make all of us sad.

WOULD IT HELP IF ...
[Write good suggestions on the back of this script]

You may want to go around the circle a second time saying, 'Would you like to tell us the idea that you liked best?' This encourages a sense of ownership of ideas by children who were unable to make their own suggestion during the round of 'Would it help if ...'.

SELECT TWO OR THREE SUGGESTIONS AS TARGETS FOR THE WEEK
[Write them here]

CELEBRATION OF ACHIEVEMENT

CLOSING GAME
<u>ELECTRIC SQUEEZE:</u> *Tell the children to hold hands right round the circle. Someone starts the current – they squeeze the hand of the person next to them. They then pass the squeeze on until it has gone right round the circle.*

DATE:	
POEM READ DURING THE LITERACY HOUR: *'I don't feel very well, Mum'*	**THEME OF TODAY'S CIRCLE TIME:** *Not wanting to go to school*

CIRCLE TIME SCRIPT

READ POEM
Read 'I don't feel very well, Mum' (page 30).

OPENING GAME

<u>FISH IN THE SEA:</u> *Move the chairs so the circle is slightly horseshoe shaped, to allow the children to move outside the circle. Then go round the circle giving the children different fish names: cod, huss, hake, squid. Give the children instructions. For example, when you say, 'Tide's out, hake!' the hake have to rush out of the circle and run round clockwise, then back in through the gap to a different chair. When they are halfway round you might say, 'Tide's turning', and they would have to reverse direction, or, 'Tidal wave coming!' and they could go in either direction back into the circle – which is the harbour. Sometimes have two sets of fish running at the same time.*
This game does help listening, but also it's great fun!

OPENING ROUND
[The beginning of the sentence]
Talk about how everybody wants to stay at home sometimes, especially if they are worried about things at school. Give the children a minute to think of a time when they have wanted to stay at home.
'I wanted to stay at home when . . .'

OPEN FORUM
From the information gained, discuss how we all, even teachers, want to stay at home sometimes. Then focus on problems that are specific to your class. You may want to take a couple of common themes, discuss them and try to think of collective solutions. You may find you will need to take some problems from this Circle Time back to your staff Circle Times.

WOULD IT HELP IF ...
[Write good suggestions on the back of this script]

SELECT TWO OR THREE SUGGESTIONS AS TARGETS FOR THE WEEK
[Write them here]

CELEBRATION OF ACHIEVEMENT

CLOSING GAME
<u>GLOOP:</u> *Tell the children you have a pot of Green Gloop in your bag, and it's really yucky. Explain that you are going to get it out and throw it at your own face. Then say you are going to pull it off your face and throw it at one of them. Then they are to pull it off their face and throw it at someone else. Explain that the best thing about this game is that they can make really disgusting noises as they pull the gloop off their face. It's always a winner.*

DATE: ....

POEM READ DURING THE LITERACY HOUR:	**THEME OF TODAY'S CIRCLE TIME:**
'New friend'	*Getting to know new people*

CIRCLE TIME SCRIPT

READ POEM
Read 'New friend' (page 31).

OPENING GAME
<u>NAMES:</u> *The children throw a bean bag to each other. Each says their name as they catch it.*

<u>CHANGE PLACES:</u> *Tell children with something in common to change places. (See page 45 for details.)*

<u>INTRODUCTIONS:</u> *Ask the children to talk to the person next to them for a minute or two, then introduce them to the circle, saying their name and reporting something they enjoy doing. They should say,*
'This is my friend … and they enjoy …'.

OPENING ROUND
[The beginning of the sentence]

'I sometimes find it hard to make new friends at school because …'
'I find it easiest to make new friends at school when I …'

OPEN FORUM
Encourage a general discussion about feeling shy, feeling no one likes you, being from another culture. Build on whatever was said in the opening round.

WOULD IT HELP IF …
[Write good suggestions on the back of this script]

This could be started by saying, 'How can we help ourselves and how can we help each other to make new friends? Practical suggestions, please! Begin, "Would it help if …".'

SELECT TWO OR THREE SUGGESTIONS AS TARGETS FOR THE WEEK
[Write them here]

CELEBRATION OF ACHIEVEMENT

CLOSING GAME
<u>ZOOM AND EEK:</u> *The children speak in turn, saying either 'Zoom' or 'Eek'. Each child has only one 'Eek', but may say 'Zoom' as many times as they choose. When a child says 'Eek', that reverses the flow. This is particularly tense if you play with a time limit!*

DATE:	YEAR: _2/3/4_
POEM READ DURING THE LITERACY HOUR: *'Questions, questions, questions!'*	**THEME OF TODAY'S CIRCLE TIME:** *Feeling fed up about things in our lives* *and not liking to mention it*

CIRCLE TIME SCRIPT

READ POEM
Read 'Questions, questions, questions!' (page 32).

OPENING GAME

<u>HARD DONE BY:</u> *Tell the children to cross the room if they have ever felt everyone else had better packed lunches than them! Or: if they have ever felt everyone knows more people in the school than they do; if they feel their shoes are not as cool as other people's; if they have ever felt hopeless at sums or found spelling long words hard. Go on until everyone has moved at least once. Play this game very fast so the children don't feel too shy to move. At the end, say, 'We all feel hopeless about something at times! Look, we've **all** moved!'*

<u>POSITIVE INTRODUCTIONS:</u> *Pair the children. Each child in the circle introduces the child who is their pair, saying, 'This is … and they are good at …'.*

<u>SHARED PROBLEMS:</u> *Now tell the pairs they have two minutes to find out something they **both** find a problem in school. Go round the circle hearing from each pair, choosing one from each pair to speak.*

OPENING ROUND
[The beginning of the sentence]

Explain that now we know we all feel fed up sometimes. The boy in the poem felt he had a horrible lunch, missed his mum, wanted a brother, felt he had no friends, couldn't read well and thought he looked a twerp! He didn't know why. Maybe it was because not enough people told him he was kind, he wasn't that bad at reading, it's OK to say you miss your mum and school uniform is, well, school uniform! So we are going to say what we are fed up about.

'This week I felt fed up about …'   'This week I felt good about …'

OPEN FORUM

Encourage the children to discuss this further and to look for ways to cheer themselves up.

WOULD IT HELP IF …
[Write good suggestions on the back of this script]

SELECT TWO OR THREE SUGGESTIONS AS TARGETS FOR THE WEEK
[Write them here]

CELEBRATION OF ACHIEVEMENT

CLOSING GAME

<u>GOLDEN SCROLL:</u> *You need a large piece of paper. Cut about 1 metre off. With a large gold marker pen, write the name of one child at the top of the paper. Then go round the circle, asking each child to say something nice about the child whose scroll it is. They may choose an attribute or a skill. Then, with proper ceremony, give the scroll to the child named.*

DATE:	YEAR: _3/4/5_
POEM READ DURING THE LITERACY HOUR: 'Goalie gloves'	**THEME OF TODAY'S CIRCLE TIME:** *Feeling jealous about the possessions of others*

CIRCLE TIME SCRIPT

READ POEM
Read 'Goalie gloves' (page 33).

OPENING GAME

CROSS THE CIRCLE IF ...: *Tell the children to cross the circle if, for example, they are wearing a school uniform jumper, have laces in their shoes, like their shoes, don't like their shoes, have ever been jealous of their friends' things, sometimes ask their mum to get them things because their friends have them.*

OPENING ROUND
[The beginning of the sentence]

Begin by saying that we all sometimes wish we had other things.

'I wish that I could have ...'

Tell the children that sometimes we forget to like the things we already have (stress the focus is on **things***, not family).* *Tell them they have twenty seconds to think of something from home that they like and it may not have a plug on it. (No computer games/playstations/Nintendo 64s.) This restriction makes for much more interesting answers.*

'I really love my ...'

OPEN FORUM

Talk about how sad it is when we forget how nice our own things are and just feel jealous of others. You could also briefly mention the importance of not mocking other people's clothes and possessions.

Ask the children how they can best remind themselves of all the nice things they already have or find ways of liking things that might not be as smart as other people's. ('But only mine go PING!') Sometimes children find the **wanting** *the exciting part; once they have whatever it is they yearned for they immediately lose interest and want something else. It will help to discuss whether they do this and, if they do, how they can learn to appreciate and celebrate their things.*

WOULD IT HELP IF ...
[Write good suggestions on the back of this script]

SELECT TWO OR THREE SUGGESTIONS AS TARGETS FOR THE WEEK
[Write them here]

CELEBRATION OF ACHIEVEMENT

CLOSING GAME

PASS THE MIME: *Ask one child to mime playing with their favourite toy, tell the person next to them what it is and pass it on to them. Then they take it as the first child's toy, change it into their choice, mime playing with it and pass it on as before. Stress that speed, accuracy and silence are key factors here.*

DATE:	YEAR: *4/5/6*
POEM READ DURING THE LITERACY HOUR: *'Now I'm in trouble too!'*	**THEME OF TODAY'S CIRCLE TIME:** *Dealing with angry feelings*

CIRCLE TIME SCRIPT

READ POEM
Read 'Now I'm in trouble too!' (page 34).

OPENING GAME
FIGHTS: *Ask the children to move if they have ever been in a fight. Ask them to move if someone has tried to wind them up; if they have felt someone might hurt them; if they have been tempted to hit someone back; and so on.*

PLASTICINE STATUES: *It is important that the children look at body language and begin to recognise how people feel from how they stand and move. Put the children into pairs round the circle. Call them A and B. Tell all the As to stand up and look like aggressive statues. Once all the As are cross statues, ask the other children to walk silently round the circle looking at the gallery of cross statues. Then say the Bs have to remodel them into something gentle. When they have remodelled them, ask them to walk round and notice the difference.*

OPENING ROUND
[The beginning of the sentence]
'When people are horrible and pick on me it makes me feel ...'
Get the children to talk about how feeling like this can make us behave. The boy in the poem feels angry and that makes him behave violently and look wild. That may make some children feel scared and perhaps sick, and they may want to stay at home.
'When I feel ... it makes me ...'

OPEN FORUM
Ask the children to talk about their responses. In the poem the boy thought it might help if he walked away, as his mum suggested, and tried not to lose his temper. Ask the children what behaviour they find works and why, and talk about behaviour that just makes things worse.

WOULD IT HELP IF ...
[Write good suggestions on the back of this script]

SELECT TWO OR THREE SUGGESTIONS AS TARGETS FOR THE WEEK
[Write them here]

CELEBRATION OF ACHIEVEMENT

CLOSING GAME
TOUCH AND GO: *Choose a child to start. This child has to walk round the outside of the circle, touch someone on the shoulder and then leave the circle. The person who was touched then gets up and touches someone else. As soon as someone has touched, they leave the circle (and go out to play or whatever). As soon as they have been touched, they stand up and touch someone else. Praise the children who are quick to touch and go.*

DATE:	YEAR: *R/1/2/3*	
POEM READ DURING THE LITERACY HOUR: *'Eczema'*	**THEME OF TODAY'S CIRCLE TIME:** *It's cruel to tease*	**SCRIPT ONE**

CIRCLE TIME SCRIPT

READ POEM
Read 'Eczema' (page 35).

OPENING GAME

<u>FRUIT SALAD:</u> *Assign different fruits to the children in sequence (e.g. apple, pear, banana, grape; apple, pear) round the circle. Call the fruit names out in random order. The children with the name called stand up and change places. Continue until everyone is sitting on a different chair from the one they started on.*

<u>POSITIVE INTRODUCTIONS:</u> *See page 54. The children will be sitting next to children other than their best friends as they have just played Fruit salad.*

OPENING ROUND

Remind the children that the child in the poem was called horrid names. Remind them that we all hate being called horrid names; sometimes it happens and it hurts.

Introduce them to a furry animal toy (hedgehog, rabbit, teddy bear – whatever you have). Tell them this little animal has been called horrid names in the playground. Ask them to say what he might have been called. The opening part of the sentence could be, 'I think people have said you are . . .'

OPEN FORUM

Say they had good ideas and the furry animal would feel sad if he had been called these names. He is pleased to be with kind children now. Continue to talk for a minute or two, asking them generally if anyone has ever been called a nasty name. If they have, say that was horrid. Then ask them to tell you kind things that we can say to each other.

WOULD IT HELP IF WE SAID ...
[Write good suggestions on the back of this script]

SELECT TWO OR THREE SUGGESTIONS AS TARGETS FOR THE WEEK
[Write them here]

You could make a wall display of the suggestions and then record success. For example, put the outline of a plant up on the wall and stick on a flower whenever a child says something that is kind.

CELEBRATION OF ACHIEVEMENT

CLOSING GAME

<u>GOODBYE:</u> *Pass the furry animal round and let each child stroke it and say, 'Goodbye.'*

<table>
<tr><td rowspan="3">SCRIPT TWO</td><td>DATE:</td><td>YEAR: 4–6</td></tr>
<tr><td>POEM READ DURING THE LITERACY HOUR:
'Eczema'</td><td>THEME OF TODAY'S CIRCLE TIME:
Failing to understand the difficulties
others live with</td></tr>
</table>

CIRCLE TIME SCRIPT

READ POEM
Read 'Eczema' (page 35).

OPENING GAME

<u>SIN BIN:</u> *Spread a large sheet of newspaper out in the centre of the circle. Make sure everyone has a piece of paper and a pencil. Ask the children to think about something they feel bad about having done in the last two weeks which they wish they could apologise for. Explain that it might be having teased someone, called someone names, shut someone out of a game, laughed at another child, ignored another child's needs – suggest eight or nine things as prompts. Give the children thirty seconds' thinking time. Ask them to write or draw what they have thought of on the piece of paper.*

OPENING ROUND
[The beginning of the sentence]

Encourage each child to say, 'I am really sorry that I ... [say whatever is on their paper] ... I wish I hadn't done this.' Ask them to put their piece of paper onto the sheet of newspaper as they say this. When everyone has spoken and put their piece of paper on the sheet, tell the children that it's nearly always possible to say sorry and make a fresh start. Wrap up the pieces of paper in the newspaper, and put them in the bin.

OPEN FORUM

Have a brief discussion about how we could prevent ourselves from making the same mistakes again. This usually involves being more aware of how it feels to be someone else. That may mean knowing more about asthma, epilepsy, hearing problems, skin problems, diabetes, mobility difficulties, birth marks and so on.

WOULD IT HELP IF ...
[Write good suggestions on the back of this script]

SELECT TWO OR THREE SUGGESTIONS AS TARGETS FOR THE WEEK
[Write them here]

CELEBRATION OF ACHIEVEMENT

CLOSING GAME

<u>SECRET BUDDIES:</u> *Have a bag containing slips of paper ready. Each slip has written on it the name of a child in the circle. Pass the bag round the circle. Each child takes a slip of paper, reads the name on it and keeps it secret. Explain that through the week the person on their slip of paper is their secret buddy. They must think of as many kind and thoughtful things they can do for them as possible. They must not tell them they are their secret buddy. The following week have a Circle Time with the opening round: 'This week I helped my secret buddy by ...'.*

DATE:	YEAR: _4/5/6/7_
POEM READ DURING THE LITERACY HOUR: 'In your dreams'	**THEME OF TODAY'S CIRCLE TIME:** Telling the truth, wanting something badly

CIRCLE TIME SCRIPT

READ POEM
Read 'In your dreams' (page 36).

OPENING GAME
FIBBING: Tell the children to swap places if they have ever told a fib, exaggerated something, or wanted something so badly they have told people they are going to get it when they meant they wished they could get it.

OPENING ROUND
[The beginning of the sentence]

'If I were Aladdin and had a magic lamp ...'

The children say what they would like the genie to fix for them. Nothing violent is allowed (e.g. 'blow up my enemies'); apart from this it can be anything; for example, make them good at sums, make them a brilliant speller, run really fast.

OPEN FORUM
Explain that we all fib sometimes, even if just to save someone's feelings. Sometimes we do it because we want to make ourselves feel more important, like the boy in the poem. Point out that it's sad that the boy felt so bad about himself and his life that he had to make up stories. Tell them about low self-esteem. Lots of people's dads don't live with them, but they don't all feel as bad as this boy does. Centre your discussion on why this boy might feel as bad as he does. Did enough people not celebrate his achievements or notice when he was good or kind? We are all responsible for others' self-esteem. How can we help each other to feel good about ourselves?

WOULD IT HELP IF ...
[Write good suggestions on the back of this script]

Don't forget to stress that we can't just say smaltzy things to each other – we have to notice the good in each other and celebrate each other's achievements, big and small, in work and behaviour.

SELECT TWO OR THREE SUGGESTIONS AS TARGETS FOR THE WEEK
[Write them here]

Build into this ways of recording targets met. Examples are giving each other stickers, getting out the Golden Scroll (see page 54), awarding certificates.

CELEBRATION OF ACHIEVEMENT

CLOSING GAME
POSITIVE INTRODUCTIONS: See page 54.

THANK YOU: Each child turns to the person on either side of them, smiles at them and says, 'Thank you for Circle Time.'

TOUCH AND GO: See page 56.

SCRIPT ONE

DATE: ....

POEM READ DURING THE LITERACY HOUR:
'The gerbil'

THEME OF TODAY'S CIRCLE TIME:
Feeling sad at the death of a pet

Don't do this too soon after the death of a pet – wait a couple of weeks.
I also suggest you have another adult in with you for this Circle Time.

CIRCLE TIME SCRIPT

READ POEM
Read 'The gerbil' (page 37).

OPENING GAME
GLOOP: *See page 52. It helps to start a serious circle with a bit of fun. Gloop is a possibility. Try to do a good deal of pantomiming around with the gloop yourself. Make the children laugh and they will feel safer because it will be obvious that you are in a good mood and feel warm towards them. It's easier to tackle difficult or painful subjects with someone who looks as if they love you than with someone who looks irritable.*

OPENING ROUND
You can say the game was good fun, but everyone knows that the class has been sad recently because … died. State clearly that it was not the fault of any of them that this happened, but nevertheless everyone is sad. Tell them we are now all going to remember … [the name of the class pet] and say one thing we will enjoy remembering about them.

[The beginning part of the sentence]
'The best thing I remember about … was …' The opening of the sentence will be influenced by the nature of the pet. A stick insect will generate a different response from a rabbit and will need a different opening sentence.

OPEN FORUM
At this point you can see how everyone is feeling. Not all class pets will prompt the same magnitude of sadness; if the snails died you can talk about why, if the rabbit died you can expect some children to cry and you will need to help them with dealing with this. You can discuss how everything eventually dies, and that for this reason we must value life and the lives of each other.

WOULD IT HELP IF … ?
[Write good suggestions on the back of this script]
You may like to look at some of the suggestions in the last chapter (page 80).

SELECT TWO OR THREE SUGGESTIONS AS TARGETS FOR THE WEEK
[Write them here]

CELEBRATION OF ACHIEVEMENT

CLOSING GAME
Ask the children which game they would like to play.

DATE: _____	THEME OF TODAY'S CIRCLE TIME:
POEM READ DURING THE LITERACY HOUR:	*Looking after pets*
'The gerbil'	*This can be helpful if your class want to keep a hamster or rabbit (or rat, or snake, or ... !)*

If a pet recently died, have a Circle Time about the death first (page 59) and then once you have decided to get a new pet you might like to hold this Circle Time.

CIRCLE TIME SCRIPT

READ POEM
Read 'The gerbil' (page 37).

OPENING GAME
Play any game that muddles children up, for example Fruit salad (page 57), Twinkle, Twinkle (page 46).
<u>KIND OR SILLY:</u> *Ask them to turn to the person who is now on their left and say, 'I think you would like it if I was kind to you and I ...'. They can say something silly or something sensible. The person on the left says 'Yes' or 'No' in response.*

OPENING ROUND
[The beginning part of the sentence]
Discuss the fact that the boy in the poem really liked the gerbil, but fed him solid glue.
Have a round that says:
'I think it would be kind to our class pet if we ...'
Look for suggestions such as fed him regularly, cleaned his cage out, tamed him etc.

OPEN FORUM
Say their suggestions are all good, and ask how they are going to make sure they happen. How can we be sure we will remember to feed him, buy his food, take him out of the cage and play with him and so on?

WOULD IT HELP IF ...
[Write good suggestions on the back of this script]
You will be encouraging suggestions that focus on personal responsibility, rotas, lists etc.
How are these to be enforced?

SELECT TWO OR THREE SUGGESTIONS AS TARGETS FOR THE WEEK
[Write them here]

CELEBRATION OF ACHIEVEMENT

CLOSING GAME
<u>KIND STATUES:</u> *Ask four children to go into the middle and make a group statue of themselves – looking like a group of monsters, or people who are cross or sad, or anything they choose that is not too pleasant (or too unpleasant!). You then ask four other children to stand up and move the statue group so they look kind and happier. Get them to concentrate on body shape rather than facial expressions. See Placticine statues (page 55) for a slight variation.*

DATE:	
POEM READ DURING THE LITERACY HOUR: *'For what we are about to receive ...'*	**THEME OF TODAY'S CIRCLE TIME:** *Healthy eating*

CIRCLE TIME SCRIPT

READ POEM
Read 'For what we are about to receive ...' (page 38).

OPENING GAME
PORK PIE: *On the back of a birthday or Christmas card picture, write the name of a well-known meal in two parts. For example, on the top half of the card write 'Baked' and on the bottom half write 'Beans'. Then cut the card in two. Other examples might be 'Scrambled/Egg', 'Pork/Pie', 'Fish/Chips', 'Rhubarb/Custard'. Make enough (you can have repeats) for each child to have one half. Shuffle all the cards together and give one to each child. The aim of the game is to move in silence round the group finding the other half. Explain that they should check if they are right by looking at the picture and checking it makes a whole. The pairs sit down as soon as they have found each other – next to one other.*

OPENING ROUND
[The beginning of the sentence]
'I think it's probably good for me to eat ...'
'My favourite food is ...'

OPEN FORUM
Encourage a discussion about the food we like to eat, the food that is good for us and the problems if these are not the same.

WOULD IT HELP IF ...
[Write good suggestions on the back of this script]
Before starting this, recap the ideas they had about what things were good to eat.

SELECT TWO OR THREE SUGGESTIONS AS TARGETS FOR THE WEEK
[Write them here]

CELEBRATION OF ACHIEVEMENT

CLOSING GAME
HOT HERONS: *The first child says a word (e.g. 'chicken'). The next child must say something that has no obvious connection to the first (e.g. 'plant pot'), and so on round the circle. If, at any point, a child thinks there is a connection between two consecutive words, they may challenge. If they can demonstrate a connection, it becomes their turn to start. This game encourages listening and thinking, and is also one to enable the anarchic free thinkers to shine!*

DATE: ....

POEM READ DURING THE LITERACY HOUR:	THEME OF TODAY'S CIRCLE TIME:
'Complacency'	*Covert cruelty*

CIRCLE TIME SCRIPT

READ POEM
Read 'Complacency' (page 39).

OPENING GAME
<u>CHANGE PLACES:</u> *See page 45.*

OPENING ROUND
[The beginning of the sentence]
You could explain that teasing and bullying can take different forms. They are not always physical.
'I've felt bullied when ...'
(remind them not to use names; they must describe the behaviour, not say who did it.)
'When I feel picked on or laughed at it makes me feel ...'

OPEN FORUM
You will soon identify the important issues for the children. Try to focus on the idea that we are all members of one another; and that if we pick on another child, or try to make them feel small or stupid, we diminish ourselves.

WOULD IT HELP IF ...
[Write good suggestions on the back of this script]
You could ask at this point, 'Is there anyone here who would like to say sorry to someone here that they know they have upset?' If someone says yes, then let them do that, and let them be direct (e.g. 'I'd like to say sorry to Nadia for laughing at her shoes.'). You could even ask the apologetic child if there is something they could do to make things better. If they suggest something, ask the other child, in this example Nadia, how they feel about the suggestion. They can accept it or reject it as they choose. Encourage any suggestions, specific or general, but pin them down to workable ones and make sure they see you write them down. Check that they know these are now promises.

SELECT TWO OR THREE SUGGESTIONS AS TARGETS FOR THE WEEK
[Write them here]

You could select more targets than usual. Explain to the children that you will talk about how much or little things have improved next Circle Time. Suggest ways of recording success (leaves on a tree, footballs in a goal, for instance).

CELEBRATION OF ACHIEVEMENT

CLOSING GAME
This may have been a painful and emotional Circle Time. Finish with some affirming games.
<u>POSITIVE INTRODUCTIONS:</u> *See page 54.*
<u>THANK YOU:</u> *See page 59.*

DATE:	
POEM READ DURING THE LITERACY HOUR: *'School trip'*	**THEME OF TODAY'S CIRCLE TIME:** *Thinking about how we behave when we* *are out of school.*

CIRCLE TIME SCRIPT

READ POEM
Read 'School trip' (page 40).

OPENING GAME
<u>BADGE GAME:</u> *Hand round blank pages. On the badge they should write their name clearly and draw a picture of something they are good at. They can wear this badge on their outing.*

<u>RANDOM GROUPING:</u> *Tell the children to move about silently inside the circle. Call out a number. The children make a group of that number of children and sit down in silence. This is repeated with a different number. Once the children can do this, set a different task; e.g., all stand touching elbows, stand back to back, form the shape of a flower.*

OPENING ROUND
Say that sometimes we can get very pleasantly excited when we are out of school. We may also get very nervous, when we are away from our usual organised routine. Sometimes in the excitement of an outing we may forget all the things that help us with managing our behaviour. This is natural. We are going to think about how we might feel during an outing, and to come up with ideas that will help us enjoy ourselves and behave as we would like.

[The beginning of the sentence]
'The best part of going on an outing is …'
'The worst part of a school outing is …'
'The time when I find it hardest to behave well is. …'

OPEN FORUM
Encourage the children to talk about the ideas they put forward.

WOULD IT HELP IF …
[Write good suggestions on the back of this script]

SELECT TWO OR THREE SUGGESTIONS AS TARGETS FOR THE OUTING AND ITS PREPARATION
[Write them here]

CELEBRATION OF ACHIEVEMENT

CLOSING GAME
<u>TRUST TRAIN:</u> *Choose five children at random. Remove their chairs. They stand one behind the other, with their hands on the shoulders of the person in front. Everyone closes their eyes apart from the driver at the back. The driver steers the train by signalling to the person infront as follows: tap on both shoulders, go forward; tap on left, go left; tap on right, go right; gentle pull, stop. The message is passed down the train, each child repeating the action of the one behind. The driver directs the train in and out of the circle.*

DATE: ....

POEM READ DURING THE LITERACY HOUR:	THEME OF TODAY'S CIRCLE TIME:
Playing with fire'	*Learn to discern*

CIRCLE TIME SCRIPT

READ POEM
Read 'Playing with fire' (page 41).

OPENING GAME

LONG TOM: *Everyone has to try to think of something that starts with the same letter as their name and if possible describes themselves – e.g. Tall Tony, Joyful Joanne. They can all help each other find good, positive names. Then ask the children to throw' the names to each other: 'Joyful Jan to Lively Laura', 'Lively Laura to Speedy Samir' etc.*

OPENING ROUND
[The beginning part of the sentence]
'I think children are unkind when they . . .'
Make sure the children think for twenty seconds before completing the sentence.

OPEN FORUM
Discuss what we should do when we hear people being unkind about each other. Tell the children that sticking up for others can be hard. Sometimes it's too hard and may be best to stay away from unkind children and play with those who are kind. They can't all be Robin Hood! But we can all learn to recognise when people are being unkind and stay away from them. It may be tempting to join with powerful or cruel people but, for a start, it's playing with fire and, secondly, it's simply not right.

WOULD IT HELP IF ...
[Write good suggestions on the back of this script]

SELECT TWO OR THREE SUGGESTIONS AS TARGETS FOR THE WEEK
[Write them here]

CELEBRATION OF ACHIEVEMENT

CLOSING GAME
CO-OPERATIVE LAPS: *See page 43.*

5 Behind Closed Doors

or
what exactly happens in your Circle Times then, Sandra?

Teaching can be a strange and paranoid profession. For whilst we give great public performances for the children in our class, we seldom get to see the show that's being given next door.

Things are even worse if you teach in an open-plan school. The noise that your class makes may give a false impression of what is happening in your room. The school layout may also make you feel desperate to keep yourself to yourself.

What is more, because we are very concerned about what colleagues think of us, of our work and our children's progress, we often keep quiet about our failures and do not share any experiences or ideas unless we are totally certain that they are good ones.

This frequently applies to our Circle Times. I know many teachers who have confided in me, 'I am not really sure if I'm doing proper Circle Time. I'm not sure what sort of things the children should be saying.'

It is no help if such a confession gets the answer, 'Oh, whatever comes from the children is fine.' We all know that the children are more likely to be fired with imagination if we ignite a few well-placed matches first.

- **Discovery, like surprise, favours the well-prepared mind.**

With this in mind, I would recommend that you have lots of **staff** Circle Times. These can run with the same script as for the children. As well as having professional issues on your agenda, you can have Circle Times about your Circle Times! For example:

'When I did a Circle Time about loneliness, I found it helped if I used … as an opening sentence.'

or:

'When we were all looking at the difficulty of transferring from the infants to the juniors and read "New friend", I found that … was a really good game to play.'

or:

'When we were thinking about our health and we read "For what we are about to receive … ", Olla had this really good idea about raw vegetables at lunchtimes.'

It's a waste not to get the best value out of our children's ideas – especially if some of them are, in fact, coping strategies that other children, or teachers, may find useful. Make a list, keep a book; we all need all the good ideas we can get!

It was for this reason that I put down some of the suggestions that children have made to me during Circle Times I have run using the poems in this book. Some of these suggestions made me want to laugh, some to cry and some to clout the child concerned! But they are only ideas, and I didn't have to act upon all of them.

I had one emerge recently during a Circle Time about chatting in class and disturbing each other: 'Would it help if we filled the chatterer's mouth with hot peppermints and then superglued their lips together?' Everyone in the year 2 class thought about this, but then decided that, on the whole, it was not the best plan – their mum would have to spend a long time in Accident & Emergency getting them unglued!

The suggestions made below are just a few notes from someone else's Circle Times. They may or may not be useful to you; much depends upon the age of the children and their individual problems. They are just there as a glimpse behind the curtain at the show going on next door!

Morning school

The ambition of this Circle Time was to help the children feel part of a warm and comforting class group that makes separation from home more bearable. These children were very young and needed plenty of help with making suggestions. I had to put in an extra round, saying, 'Let's go round again and say which suggestion we liked the best.' This meant the children all *owned* a suggestion even if they were unable to make one. Suggestions included:

- Would it help if we waved goodbye through the window and not at the door?
- Would it help if we sang a special 'Hello' song every morning before we started?
- Would it help if you told us as soon as we came in about some of the nice things we were going to do during the day?
- Would it help if we sat in a circle for register and sang a morning song then?

Book corner

This was a Circle Time for a year 1 class who were finding sharing difficult. This particular poem was written with a little girl called Rhidi; she wanted to share but was unsure how to make a start!

During the Circle Time it was decided that each child was going to offer to share one specific thing with another child, not their best friend, during the coming week.

I promised that each time I spotted them sharing as they had offered, I would praise them and stick a flower on the cut-out green stalks which would be stuck to the wall. When complete we would have a beautiful bouquet of fifteen roses, one for each pair. At that point I told the class they had been presented with this beautiful bouquet because they had been so wonderful. They had twenty minutes' parachute games at the end of the week as a special treat.

I knew I would have to keep reminding them of their target when I thought failure was likely. I tried to ensure success by praising the children who were remembering, not criticising those who may have simply forgotten.

We made one practical decision – to use a couple of floor cushions to make a kind of sofa in the book corner.

Dressing-up box

This was another sharing and turn-taking Circle Time. Among the 'Would it helps' we had:

- Would it help if when we chose what we were going to do we asked someone to share the activity with us and used the words 'Would you like to share the ... with me?'
- Would it help if we didn't bring things into school unless we knew we were going to share them with lots of people, not just our best friends?
- Would it help if every time we shared something with someone else we gave ourselves a star on the night sky? (This involved using LDA reusable target sheets.)
- Would it help if we tried to see how many of the sharing words we could catch ourselves saying in the next three days and keep a count?
- Would it help if we tried hard not to say any of the not sharing words and said sorry if we found ourselves saying them?
- Would it help if we made a scrapbook of all the songs and poems and hymns about sharing that we can find?

Put your hand up

This is the result of several Circle Times with different classes – possibly several hundred!

- Would it help if we had a quiet sign, such as the teacher raising her hand if she wants quiet rather than having to shout? (This is used by Rainbow and Brownie leaders.)
- Would it help if we put our hand *down* while someone else is speaking?
- Would it help if we were very quiet while you were telling us what to do?
- Would it help if we didn't tip our chairs so you didn't have to tell us off about that all the time?
- Would it help if we looked at the person who was speaking?
- Would it help if we didn't fiddle with the person next to us when we were sitting on the carpet?
- Would it help if we put our hand up and didn't call out when we want to say something?
- Would it help if we didn't wave our hands like flags while we had them in the air?

- ▶ Would it help if we didn't talk when someone else is speaking?
- ▶ Would it help if we don't shout out and interrupt each other?

The Lego pencil

I get very tired of people always accusing each other of 'nicking' equipment. I also get fed up with the sort of 'borrowing' in which there may have been no intention of keeping what was borrowed, but there was no intention of giving it back properly either – it was just a matter of borrowing and casually mislaying something.

I think a Circle Time about this can bring it to children's attention that they must be more aware of the things that pass through their hands.

- ▶ Would it help if we had a basket of pencils in the middle of each table and a table monitor to check it each morning?
- ▶ Would it help if we had a rule that we always gave everything back before going out to play or to another classroom?
- ▶ Would it help if we didn't bring things to school if we were worried about people wanting to borrow them?
- ▶ Would it help if we had a PE kit check once a week and told our mummies if something was missing? (Because mummies aren't psychic and don't always know that plimsolls have become too small or a T-shirt has gone missing!)
- ▶ Would it help if we asked our teacher to shave about two centimetres off one side of the top of each pencil and we wrote our name on this shaved bit with a biro? If we didn't want to spoil our pencil like this, perhaps it's too precious for school.
- ▶ Would it help if we had a book in which we wrote down things we borrowed from other classes and things that were borrowed from us?
- ▶ Would it help if we remembered to give things straight back as soon as we had finished with them?
- ▶ Would it help if we remembered that if we borrow something, that does not make it ours?

Story time

Learning to concentrate and force your mind to pay attention to someone else is hard for all of us, and it has to be learned early if school is to be a useful experience.

When I read this poem to one class, a little girl in year 1 said, 'My ears keep listening but sometimes my mind goes outside.' I had great sympathy with that.

These are some ideas children have had:

- Would it help if we tried to sit in silence for the first five minutes of every lesson, during the bit where you tell us what to do?
- Would it help if we had a big sign, maybe a big ear, that any of us could put up when it got too noisy for us in class?
- Would it help if we tried to remember to look at the person who was talking to us?
- Would it help if we played lots of looking and listening games?
- Would it help if you played peaceful music when you wanted us to work quietly on our own? (I have frequently heard this suggested during Circle Times about listening and concentrating.)
- Would it help if we remembered not to fiddle with each other when we are supposed to be listening?
- Would it help if you had a special sign or signal such as a drum or chime bar that you could bang to tell us to stop dreaming and listen? Then you wouldn't have to shout at us all the time. (This is also a frequent suggestion. One teacher I worked with used a rain stick as a result of this suggestion and found it worked very well. The children could see it because it was big and became quiet quickly because they wanted to concentrate on hearing the gentle noise it made.)

Who's a bully?

I honestly don't think anyone ever sets out in life to be a vile, unlikable bully. Why they end up like this has been the subject matter for countless books, studies and conferences. I think as a profession we are much better at getting to grips with this problem now than we were when I first started teaching.

The reason for writing this poem was to try to encourage children to be aware that sometimes they are being a bully, even though they don't mean to be and don't even know they are. They have to learn to think about the effect of their behaviour on the lives and happiness of others, and this poem was to provide one of the starting points for discussion.

- ● Would it help if we let other people share our things?
- ● Would it help if we took turns in the Wendy House/home corner/book corner/Dinosaur Den?
- ● Would it help if we tried to say 'Yes' when people asked to use things, not 'No'?
- ● Would it help if we asked nicely and said 'Please' when we wanted something?
- ● Would it help if we remember the Golden Rule, 'Do be gentle: Don't hurt any one'? (School Golden Rules are very helpful. If your school does not use them, see *Turn Your School Round* by Jenny Mosley, published by LDA.)

Friends

If you are doing this circle with year R or year 1, you may have to make quite a few suggestions to help them. This is because feeling abandoned is a big problem for young children and they don't yet know many good techniques for overcoming it.

- ● Would it help if we looked after people who look sad?
- ● Would it help if we looked out for people who looked sad?
- ● Would it help if we asked people who are on their own if they would like to play?
- ● Would it help if we all knew lots of playground games so anyone could join in a game?
- ● Would it help if we always played with lots of different people so we didn't feel too bad when some of our friends don't want to play with us?
- ● Would it help if we tried not to say unkind things to each other?
- ● Would it help if we knew people from other classes so we could play with them?
- ● Would it help if no one was allowed to 'own' the game?
- ● Would it help if there wasn't always a 'Captain' in a game?

(This was a local difficulty, but until the Circle Time none of the staff had any idea this was a problem.)

I don't feel very well, Mum

- ◐ Would it help if we had a collage of photographs of our mums, dads or carers on the wall of the classroom so we could look at it when we felt a bit gloomy?
- ◐ Would it help if at the end of each day we sat in a circle, not for a Circle Time but just for a chat, and you told us one or two nice things that were going to happen tomorrow, so we had something to look forward to when it was morning.
- ◐ Would it help if our mums or dads, or whoever puts us to bed at night, asked us to tell them about whatever it was that we were looking forward to just before they kissed us goodnight? Then we could be reminded of this in the morning.

These are all valid suggestions, but the best suggestion for this problem is to have a staff Circle Time to share ideas and, if possible, a parents' Circle Time too. I know this sounds ambitious, but it's not impossible.

Ask parents if they would like to arrive twenty minutes early at the end of the school day, for a Circle Time. Find a way for your class to join another class for that twenty minutes (perhaps they could all watch a short video or a schools programme).

Don't make parents feel bad if they can't make it, but hope to get five or six who can. You may be lucky and get more!

Run the Circle Time according to a script, as for any other Circle Time.

I suggest a simple changing places game to break the ice, then an opening sentence of 'I sometimes find it difficult to get my child to come to school when ...'.

The Open Forum should spring from the things said during the round. After that have the usual 'Would it help ...' round.

If you want, you can say either 'Would it help ...' or 'I find it helps if ...'.

Write down all the good suggestions (and then share them with colleagues).

Try to have a round of thank yous, and close with a favourite game of your class.

Try to make this fun and productive. Make everyone feel great because they made the effort to come along, smile a great deal and be really warm and welcoming.

You may want to do this again for some other topic, so you want it to get a good press in the playground from the parents.

New friend

This is a useful Circle Time poem for the beginning of a year or at the change from infant to junior or First to Middle School.

- ◗ Would it help if we all knew lots of the same playground games? We don't yet, because we were all in different classes last year.
- ◗ Would it help if we remembered to use the Friendship Stop? (The bench the children sit on to indicate they need someone to play with.)
- ◗ Would it help if we arranged to play with someone *before* we went outside for morning break?
- ◗ Would it help if we made badges with our names on and drew pictures of things we liked doing and wore them for a few weeks, until we knew each other?
- ◗ Would it help if we had a special sharing area of the playground where we could take football cards for swapping? And we could do our sticker books together. This way we could talk to each other.
- ◗ Would it help us make new friends if we had more lunchtime clubs and we asked all the children in the school what clubs they would like?
- ◗ Would it help if when you wanted to join the football you joined in a pair to keep the sides even, so people didn't keep saying 'Go away' all the time?
- ◗ Would it help if there was a bench next to the football so if you didn't have anyone you knew to make a pair, someone else who wanted to play football could see you sitting there and join you to make a pair?
- ◗ Would it help us play with new people if we had some big cards with games printed on them that we could get to

remind us of games and their rules, and when we got a card we held it up to show we were going to start a new game and anyone could play?

Questions, questions, questions!

You can use this Circle Time to address any small but real worries children may have.

Often children have worries that they think are entirely specific to them and therefore they don't like to mention them. If they realise through Circle Time that their worry is shared by other people, this can not only make them feel less isolated; it can also get the worry sorted out.

The same principle also applies to staff Circle Times.

- ◗ Would it help if we sometimes had Circle Times about the really little things as well as the big things that upset us?
- ◗ Would it help if we got our Golden Scroll out every week for a different child?
- ◗ Would it help if we remembered Tell-A-Good-Tale every day? (This is when children sit with you on the carpet after lunch break and, instead of letting them tell you about all the awful things that happened during the lunch break, you say you will only listen to them telling you tales of good and kind things that happened to them or their friends. This is enjoyable and pleasantly habit forming. You must be strict; there must be no bad tales at all and plenty of praise and thanks for the kind actions and the kind tale-tellers.)
- ◗ Would it help if we had a 'This is my work and I'm proud of it' noticeboard in our class too? (This is a noticeboard with a big hand-written sign in the middle saying, 'This is my work and I'm proud of it.' The children can pin on this board any work that they are proud of; they do not ask for your permission. If they think it's good, then that's fine; it goes up. This helps children to validate their own work, so that they do not always need the approval of others.)
- ◗ Would it help if we got a lot more stickers just for trying?
- ◗ Would it help if we put up photographs of ourselves and underneath we all wrote nice things about that person?

○ Would it help if when we were worried about something we wrote it on a card and put it in the Agenda Box? (This is a box like a post-box, in which anyone can put suggestions for Circle Times. It can be used by children, staff, parents – indeed, anyone who has something that is worrying them that they would like taken to a Circle Time.)

Goalie gloves

I wrote this poem because so many children seemed to be always wanting the things their friends had, and then as soon as they had them too, they wanted something else. It seemed that it was the wanting that was the exciting part. Possibly, as well, they enjoyed the power struggle with a parent to get the item.

We decided to have a Circle Time about how we could teach ourselves to like the things we already had. We also wanted to revisit some old things, remember why we wanted them and relearn to love them.

I have known sad Circle Times when children have expressed great regret at having badgered their parents for demanding pets, such as dogs, and admitted that then they have not really looked after them. They have used the circle to express their remorse and decide to be more responsible in the future.

○ Would it help if we made a list of our favourite things?
○ Would it help if we didn't laugh at each other's things?
○ Would it help if we remembered the Golden Rule, 'Do be kind. Don't hurt other people's feelings'?
○ Would it help if we had a Favourite Toys Day and could bring our things in to show each other and say why they are special to us?
○ Would it help if we sometimes brought in our own favourite things for Golden Time and shared them?
○ Would it help if we got out our Christmas presents and set them up and looked at them again, at home?
○ Would it help if we got out our birthday presents and looked at them again, at home?
○ Would it help if we made a display in our classroom of our favourite toys? Just for a few days!
○ Would it help if we took pictures of this display and made a scrapbook of our favourite things?

- Would it help if we had a 'Special things showing time' and had to say what we thought was good about the 'special thing' brought in by the person next to us in the circle?
- Would it help if I played with my dog a bit more often?
- Would it help if I took the hamster out of its cage and tamed it again?

Now I'm in trouble too!

Even quite young children will be able to contribute suggestions to this circle as they will have been getting advice about dealing with aggression (theirs and others) since playgroup.

They may make suggestions such as:

- Would it help if I didn't get involved in a discussion with the people who are bullying [this is what it is] me?
- Would it help if I told a teacher or lunchtime supervisor? (Not always; sometimes they say disastrous things like, 'Oh! It's not that bad,' or 'I expect it's six of one and half a dozen of the other.' Even if that's the case, a request for help is going unanswered.
- Would it help if we just walked away and found a game we enjoyed and played that?
- Would it help if I did as my dad said and punched their lights out? (We have to stress that violence in school is quite out of the question.)
- Would it help if we had lots of things to do in the playground? (There is a whole raft of things that can be done here, ideas for which are available in *Turn Your School Round* and *Effective IEPs through Circle Time*: teaching playground games, having teams of older children help with dishing out equipment, other teams to play with and care for the younger children, different games for different days, no big games days – all sorts of ideas. It also has to be said that it is important to work on the self-esteem of the child who is bullied, so bullies don't scent blood when they are around.)
- Would it help if we stopped the fighting and asked the two who are upset what seems to be the matter?

I have often heard children make the last suggestion above. Teachers get very anxious about this idea. They often feel they are the only people who can mediate in school, and then they don't do it! Circle Time is all about handing over power to children, it's scary stuff!

If you have children in year 5 who are suggesting that they talk to people who are upset, then I think it would be very sensible if you looked into getting proper mediation training for the whole year. It may well be one of the best training investments you ever make.

In the short term, however, not rising to the bait, walking away and finding a friend and a good game is probably the best way of avoiding problems.

Eczema

I have provided two Circle Time scripts, one for younger children and one for older.

The younger children tend to respond to the sudden realisation that they may have hurt others with unthinking teasing by wanting to be kinder. This can result in rather overwhelming 'petting' of the child who has been upset. This doesn't matter as long as you put in place a good system for noticing the kindness of others.

You might try 'Kind hands'. All the children in the class or school cut out hands from paper. When they are spotted being kind, they may put their name or a description of their kind act on their hand and put the hand up on the wall.

Try to get a nice wavy line of kind hands stretching all around the classroom. You can then honestly tell the children that their class is held in kind hands – their hands. And they will see this is true.

- Would it help if we said, 'Would you like to play with me?' when someone was in a bad way with their problem?
- Would it help if we reminded each other every week of the things that other people are good at? Maybe as a Circle Time round?
- Would it help if we said in Tell-A-Good-Tale when someone had been kind or helped us, especially if it was when we felt sad or poorly?
- Would it help if we noticed when someone was good at their work or had tried really hard?
- Would it help if we said, 'Cheer up, come and join us' if someone looked sad?

The older children made suggestions such as the following:

- ◗ Would it help if we all knew more about illnesses such as eczema, psoriasis or asthma; or sight problems, hearing problems, speech difficulties, mobility problems or any other problems we might meet? Especially once we get to secondary school.
- ◗ Would it help if we made a list of all the problems, big or small, we have between us in our class? (These might include some of the list above but also include diabetes, epilepsy, birth marks.) Maybe we could talk about the **real** problems associated with these difficulties as people who are sufferers. This might help us be more sympathetic.

In your dreams

When I was a child I can remember telling the class I had swum a mile. I hadn't and I knew I hadn't. But I didn't feel I was lying or even exaggerating; I was quite a good swimmer and might even have been able to manage a mile. What I was doing was trying to increase my own store of public esteem. At the time I was very miserable. My father had died a couple of years before, I didn't feel as if I was doing as well at school as I could, and I was being mercilessly bullied by children who were much richer and didn't have home-grown haircuts. So I invented something to bump up my flagging supplies of public esteem. I was punished for lying, and grew even more depressed!

As this was something that burned itself into my brain, I have always been very aware of children who tell this sort of lie. They are simply the result of a child doing something for themselves that we should be doing for them.

It is up to each of us in the class to celebrate all achievements, praise effort and notice and applaud triumphs, however small. We have the chance to do this in Circle Time, during the 'Celebration of achievement'. We must also be sure to do this through stickers, certificates, praise in assembly, letters home or indeed any way we can to help children feel as happy and valued as possible.

There are plenty of ideas in the books mentioned in the resources section at the back of this book (see page 86).

Some children have a number of things that will deplete their self-esteem 'bank account'. Home or family difficulties are just one of them. We can't do anything to put those problems right, but we can be sure a child still has good self, and public, esteem.

○ Would it help if we had a place on the classroom wall for all of our certificates for good work, and had copies of our certificates to take home?

○ Would it help if we made a list throughout the week of things we were going to praise in Circle Time so we didn't forget when it came to that bit of our Circle Time?

○ Would it help if we remembered to praise each other and not just our best friends when they get things right or do well? (It's the job of each of us to notice the good things we all do, not just the teacher's job.)

○ Would it help if we remembered to use the 'This is my work and I'm proud of it' noticeboard and learnt that it's OK to celebrate our own real achievements?

Have plenty of staff Circle Times on whole school approaches to celebrating achievement in as many ways as possible.

Think of self-esteem as currency and try to make your school and each child in it as rich as possible!

The gerbil

This is a difficult Circle Time. Not only may children be upset about the death of a much-loved pet, but there is also the difficulty that children will naturally start to think about other deaths. You may feel you have opened up a dreadful can of worms. Sometimes as teachers we have to be brave and face these difficulties. If you are facing them during Circle Time, you have a big advantage. You have the tight organisation of a Circle Time script to help you. This means that you will not feel cast adrift into a mire of scary, unfocused debate about death, but can use the script to take you through the discussion and sadness.

If there is a child who becomes noticeably upset by the subject, perhaps because of the recent death of a family member, I suggest you ask if they would like to go outside and talk to the other adult about this immediately. This is why I have suggested in the script that you may have another adult with you for this poem.

I have had this happen in a Circle Time (see *Effective IEPs through Circle Time*, page 93). When the distressed child has left, carry on with the Circle Time and don't be distracted into a discussion about the child's personal grief. It is very important to remember to stick to the script, as for any other Circle Time.

Death is a difficult discussion subject for children. It is probably best to say that they will come to understand that everything on the planet eventually dies, and that dying is part of living. It is most unlikely to be their fault and they mustn't feel guilty about a death. We do all have a responsibility to care for our pets to the best of our ability, though, as often we have made them totally dependent on us.

Some suggestions I have heard children make to help with this problem are the following:

- Make a collage of pictures of the pet and put them in a photograph frame. (Don't use clip frames as they are dangerous if they get knocked off the wall.)
- Compile a book of treasured memories.
- Have a spot in the school garden where pets are buried. (Although this sounds a bit gruesome, it is a favourite suggestion. I have done this and found that it helps. The children pass the spot with its marker and remember the pet. As time goes on they realise that they are able to remember the pet, but the pain they felt at the time of its death is passing. I think this helps children realise that they will get over the initial intense upset, although they never forget the pet or what it meant to them. Knowing and feeling this can help them realise that they will be able to survive other, much more painful deaths.)
- You could read them stories from other cultures and from the past that show how other people have come to understand dying.

For what we are about to receive ...

This Circle Time is good fun. The children come up with lots of very worthy suggestions, but they don't really want to do any of them! Still, this is a much better way of looking at the topic of 'our bodies' than haranguing them about a 'healthy balanced diet' – which no one, not even the teacher, really wants to hear about.

- Would it help if we ate one thing each day which we knew was good for us?
- Would it help if we banned crisps at break time and brought in fruit instead?
- Would it help if we don't have batter on school fish?

- Would it help if we only had buns for dessert once a week?
- Would it help if we asked the school cooks to a Circle Time about how difficult it is to do the lunches?
- Would it help if we had oven chips instead of fried chips?
- Would it help if we took more exercise at home?
- Would it help if we had salad twice a week even in the winter?
- Would it help if sometimes we had the school dinner vegetables raw?

Complacency

- Would it help if we simply remembered that if you can't say something nice, you shouldn't say anything at all?
- Would it help if we moved our place in class more often so we got to know different children?
- Would it help if we had more clubs so we could meet different children and realise that children who were hopeless at football might be great at chess?
- Would it help if we simply remembered to think, 'If someone is not happy, what can I do to help, and is their unhappiness anything to with my behaviour?'?

Helping children come to a greater understanding of their own behaviour is difficult. It can help if you bring the issue to the front of their minds whenever you read books or stories about unhappy children or loners. They need to learn that it can feel great to be part of the in-crowd, but that has to be tempered by feelings of empathy towards those who may be less socially skilled.

School trip

Having stood in front of countless classes in both primary and secondary schools and delivered the 'no fighting on the bus, no shouting out, it disturbs the driver (and me!); and stay with your group when we arrive' talk, I decided it was probably better to get the class to decide for themselves what would make a school outing successful – hence this poem.

I have found since that the suggestions given are always sound and often rather salutary for the accompanying adults.

- ▶ Would it help if we sat with our group and with our group leader on the coach so they know us and we know them a bit better by the time we get there?
- ▶ Would it help if we played some quiet concentrating games on the coach with our group, such as 'I spy' and 'I went to market and I bought an apple, a banana, a carrot etc.'?
- ▶ Would it help if we played 'Consequences' or 'Picture consequences' with our group on the coach as you can do this passing pieces of paper round the group?
- ▶ Would it help if were allowed to sing some good songs on the coach that we know from school such as 'Give me oil in my lamp', 'One more step along the road I go', 'There were ten in the bed', and 'I can sing a rainbow'?
- ▶ Would it help if we had the words written down in a little song book so we could all sing along (older groups only)?
- ▶ Would it help if some of the games were a competition between groups; for example, who could sing the sweetest, who could sing the quietest, who could sing in a French accent?
- ▶ Would it help if we got a book of pencil and paper games before we went and practised some of them in break time during the week before we went?
- ▶ Would it help if all the grown-ups sat with the children and helped us play games on the coach and didn't sit with each other and just chat? (A good suggestion and one made to me several times by children, but one which has never proved popular with the grown-ups, although it pays fantastic dividends if you persuade them to do it.)
- ▶ Would it help if each group had a 'Be silent' sign such as a hand in the air that we could use once we were there?
- ▶ Would it help if each group leader had a different coloured baseball cap or scarf so we could see them easily and not worry about getting lost?

Playing with fire

The following suggestions were made:

- Would it help if we walked away from people when they were being horrible about others?
- Would it help if we were brave and said, 'That isn't kind'?
- Would it help if we told the teacher?
- Would it help if we put a note in the Circle Time Agenda Box and have a Circle Time about why people are cruel to others?

Epilogue

I hope that through the poems and the Circle Times in this book children and adults will learn to pass their time in school in a way that helps them feel closer to each other and better about themselves. I have always believed that the road to hell is paved not just with good intentions but with good intentions with no system. Circle Time is the system that might help you to put in place all the good intentions you have for the happiness and wellbeing of your classroom and your staff room. Think of Circle Time as practical love.

I should like to leave you with this quotation from an article written by Robert Fulghum, Grafton Books, 1989. It's called 'Everything I needed to know I learned in Kindergarten'. I was given it at a conference where I was speaking two weeks after I finished writing this book and it seemed then, as now, to sum it all up very well.

"Most of what I needed to know about how to live and what to do and how to be, I learned in Kindergarten. Wisdom was not at the top of the Graduate School mountain, but there in the sandbox at Nursery School. These are the things I learned.

Share everything. Play fair. Don't hit people. Put things back where you found them. Clean up your own mess. Don't take things that aren't yours. Say sorry when you hurt somebody. Wash your hands before you eat. Flush. Learn some and think some and play and work some, every day. When you go out into the world, watch for traffic, hold hands and stick together. Be aware of wonder. Remember the little seed in the plastic cup. The roots go down and the plant goes up and no-one really knows how or why, but we are all like that. Goldfish and hamsters and white mice and even the little seed in the plastic cup – they all die.

Everything you need to know is in there somewhere. Ecology and politics and sane living. Think what a better world it would be if we all – the whole world – had a basic policy to always put things back where we found them and clean up our own messes. And it's still true, no matter how old you are, when you go out into the world, it is best to hold hands and stick together."

Enjoy your Circle Times and don't forget, as a class and as a staff, hold hands and stick together.

Sarratt Bottom, 1998

Appendix
Resources

Training – Jenny Mosley Inset Courses

The following courses are available from a team of highly qualified and experienced consultants who can be contacted through:

Jenny Mosley Consultancies
8 Westbourne Road
Trowbridge
Wiltshire
BA14 0AJ
Tel: 01225 767157
Fax: 01225 755631

Promoting Happier Lunchtimes
Turn Your School Round – an introduction
A whole School Approach to building self-esteem through Circle
    Time
Assessing the effectiveness of your self-esteem, anti-bullying and
    positive behaviour policies
Raising morale through team-building
Practical activities to maintain and develop the power of Circle Time
Equal Opportunities
Curriculum enrichment
Drama and creative arts
Play therapy: an introduction course
Writing effective IEPs through Circle Time
Poetry and Circle Time

Training Support for your workplace

The Jenny Mosley Consultancies well trained personnel, experienced in all aspects of the Quality Circle Time model who are available to visit your work place to give courses and workshops to all your teaching and support staff.

We run both 'closure' and 'in-school' days. In the closure day, all staff, teachers, lunch time supervisors, ancillary and administration staff are all invited to participate in a day that focuses on aspects of the Circle Time Model including team-building and developing moral values through Golden Rules, Incentives and Sanctions and ideas for Happier Lunchtimes.

During the in-school day the school does not close and the Circle Time method is demonstrated with whole classes of children observed by a range of staff. In addition to this Circle Time meetings are held for lunchtime supervisors and an Action Plan for the schools considered with key members of staff.

Training the Trainer Courses

Key people may be trained either to go back to their school or their LEA as certified trainers responsible for supporting all adults and children in their community through the Jenny Mosley model. Currently Fife City Council are hosting a series of on-going five day courses led by Jenny Mosley. For further information contact Gordon Lennox on 01592 414600.

Quality Circle Time Training Manuals and Resources

Goldthorpe, M. (1998) *Effective IEPs through Circle Time*, LDA
Mosley, J. (1993) *Turn Your School Round*, LDA.
Mosley, J. (1997) *Quality Circle Time*, LDA.
Mosley, J. (1996) *Golden Rules Posters*, LDA.
Mosley, J. (1996) *Class Target Sheets*, LDA.
Mosley, J. (1996) *Reward Certificates*, LDA.
Mosley, J. (1996) *Responsibility Badges*, LDA.
Mosley, J. (1996) *Stickers*, LDA.
Mosley, J. *Guidelines for Midday Supervisory Assistants in Primary Schools to Create Happier Lunchtimes*, Wiltshire Education Advisory Services, County Hall, Trowbridge, Wiltshire.

Mosley, J. (1996) *Photocopiable Materials for use with the Jenny Mosley Circle Time Model*, Positive Press.

Other Useful Resources

Bliss, T. and Robinson, G. (1995) *Developing Circle Time*, Lucky Duck Publications.

Bliss, T. and Tetley, J. (1995) *Circle Time*, Lucky Duck Publications.

Curry, M. and Broomfield, C. (1995) *Personal and Social Education for Primary Schools through Circle Time*, NASEN Enterprises Ltd.

Fitzpatrick, P, Clarke, K. and Higgins, P. (1994) *Self-Esteem*, The Chalkface Project.

O'Brian, T. (1998) *Promoting Positive Behaviour*, David Fulton.

'Playgrounds in the Primary School', *Teaching Today*, BSS, PO Box 7, London.

Feest, G. (1992) *Listening Skills: Activities for Primary School Children and Their Teachers*, Southgate Publishers Ltd.

Kingston Friends Workshop Group (1985) *The Handbook of Kingston Friends Workshop Group*, Ways and Means: An Approach to Problem Solving.

The Guide Association publish several activity packs for Brownies, Guides and Rainbows, appropriate for use with primary aged children. Atlantic Street, Broadheath, Altringham, Cheshire, WA14 5EQ.

The Gamesters Handbooks 1 and 2, by Donna Brandes, Hutchinson, are now out of print but are full of good ideas if you can get your hands on one!